Preschool Prodigies

CHAPTER SEVEN

By: Robert and Samantha Young

Illustrations: Robert Young with art licensed at FreePik.com

Published by: Young Music, LLC

ISBN: 978-0999210154
Copyright © 2017
Preschool Prodigies and Young Music, LLC
2358 Dutch Neck Road
Smyrna, DE 19977

Prodigies Playground
THIS BOOK BELONGS TO:

_____

Dear families & teachers,

Welcome back to Preschool Prodigies! Oh how far we've come!!

Chapter Seven will focus on the three major chords, C, F and G (I IV V). Even though chords are a more difficult concept, they are essential to developing a strong sense of pitch. Plus, with this workbook, the Playground videos, and all the prior lessons, you and your kids are ready for the challenge.

To keep your chord practice fresh, this Chapter features a lot of cut-outs and manipulatives that you can use to engage in all kinds of chord-based activities.

In this chapter, we'll also learn some simple chord patterns, or progressions like the Blues.

If your kids have a hard time with chords, simplify the chords to just the root notes (C, F and G). Then work in other bells from there.

If they're having an easy time with chords, and playing the songs accurately, challenge them to jam on each chord a bit. In other words, experiment with the rhythm or the order of notes a bit. If you're jamming, make sure to still change chords when the song does!

Don't forget that it takes preschool children roughly 3-4 months to internalize each chord. With this in mind, it's important that you repeat the lessons multiple times over multiple weeks and months. Even after you've completed the workbooks, continue practicing with the videos and the sheet music until your kids are singing in tune and playing with accuracy.

Ideally, your kids should be able to play the sheet music, with steady timing, without the help of the video. At the highest level, aim to memorize the song so that students can perform it without the sheet music! Then throw a recital to show off their talents.

If your kids get tired of a particular section or concept, it's okay to move on, but you MUST come back and continue to master the concepts. Replay the videos and the sheet music often as continued practice and repetition is key to mastery.

Happy Musicing,

– Mr. Rob & the Prodigies Team

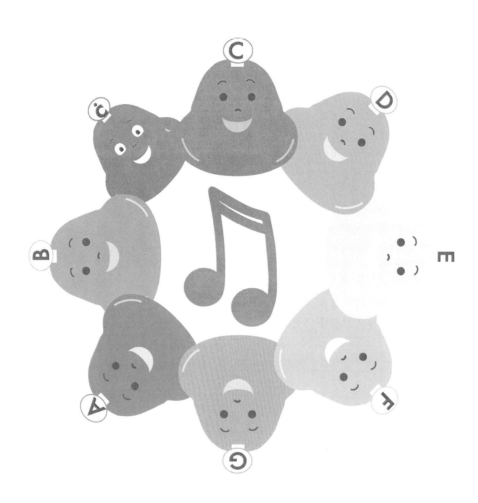

Chapter 7 ♫ Section 1: Fa La Do Slide ♫ Lesson Guide

Objective
By the end of this section, students should be able to associate the F major chord with the notes: c, A & F.

Overview
In this section, students learn the F major chord.

Essential Question
How can a student play an F major chord?

Instruction Tips
There is a lot of cutting in this section. You may want to consider asking students or parents to cut out the cubes ahead of time, in order to save time during the lesson.

Materials
- F Bell • High c Bell • A Bell
- Green Crayon • Red Crayon
- Purple Crayon
- Fa La Do Slide Video Access
- Workbook pages: 6-19
- Scissors
- Tape

Table of Contents

Fa La Do Slide Song Sheets	6
Building the F Chord	9
Write a Song Using the F Chord	10
I-IV Progressions	11
Missing Chord Pieces	12
F, c & A Cubes	13
Cube Stacking	19

Complementary Activities
Have your students write a song as a class using all of their cubes. Tell them they can add their cubes in any order that they want in order to come up with a collaborative song. At the end, play the song as a class.

Section 7.1 Video Annotations

0:00 Explain to students that this is a warm up with the notes Fa, La and Do. They should take out their F, A and high c bells.

1:26 Mr. Rob sings the Solfège hand-signs instead of the colors of the bells.

2:13 Mr. Rob sings the scale degrees instead of the Solfège hand-signs.

2:49 Students play two notes at the same time

3:38 Pause here and ask your learner which harmony they think sounds the best.

3:44 Students play all three notes to make up the F chord.

4:22 Mr. Rob explains chords and the F major chord or IV chord.

Fa La Do Slide
Lesson 7.1
☆☆☆☆☆

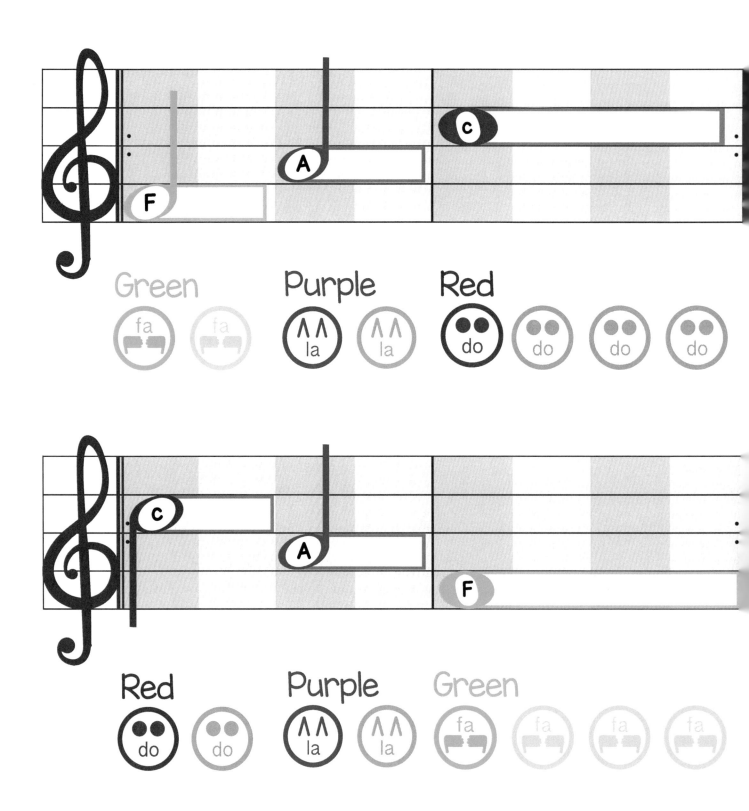

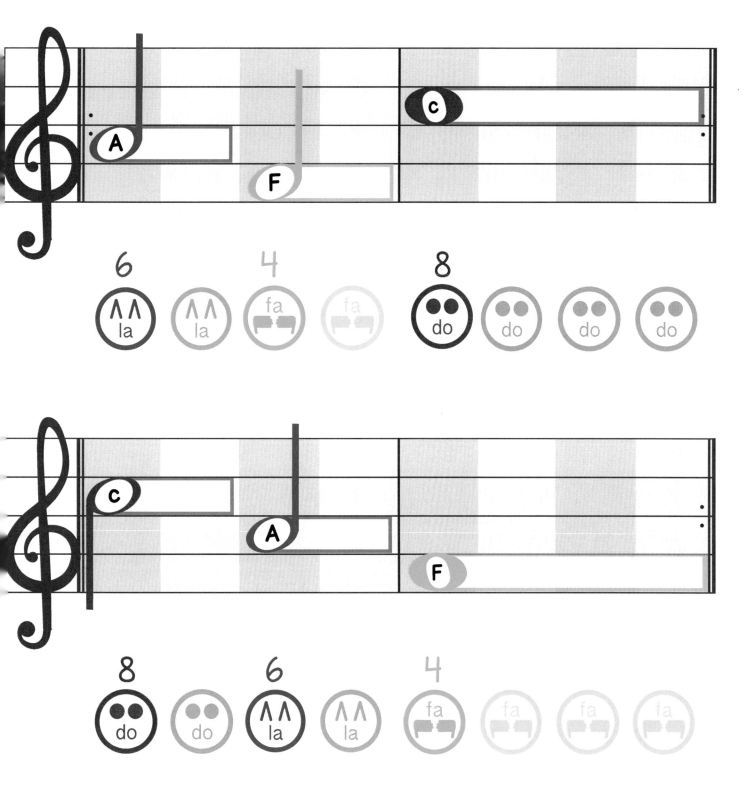

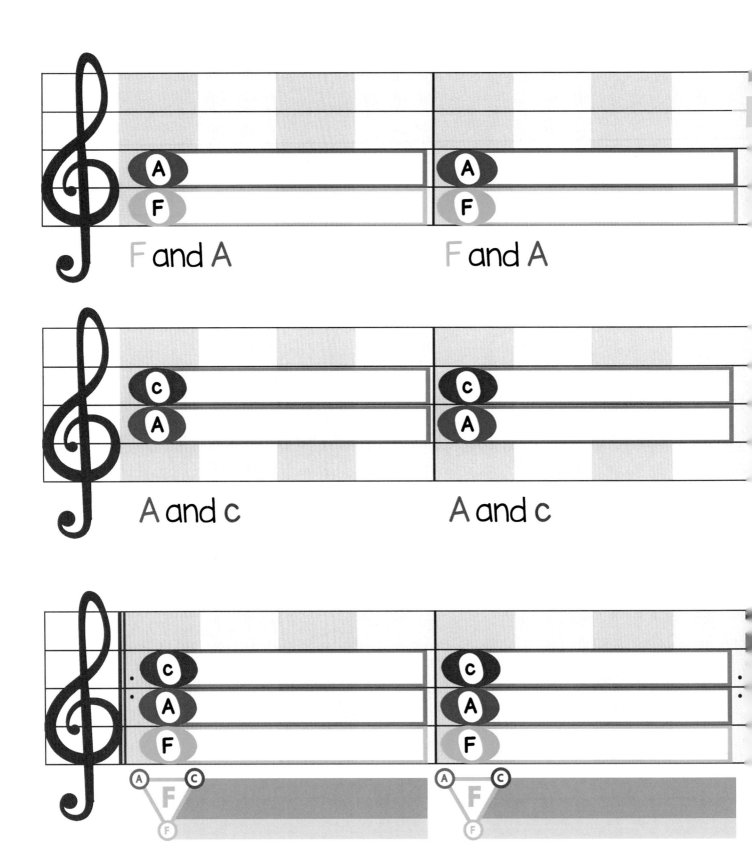

F and A   F and A

A and c   A and c

Building the F Chord

Let's learn how to build an F chord.
We already know that a chord is a group of musical notes.
If it's an F Chord, we can guess that it starts on the note F.
But how do we find out what the next note is?

1. Pick a starting note. Let's use F. This will be our ROOT NOTE. Our chord will grow up from the root, just like plants grow up from their roots!

2. From the Root Note, SKIP UP. You will land on A, which is the next note in your chord.

Play them together!

3. From your second note (A) SKIP UP again! You'll land on High c, which is the last note in your chord.

Congratulations!
You built an F Chord.

Write a Song Using

Write a melody using Fa, La and Do. Then play it on your instrument.

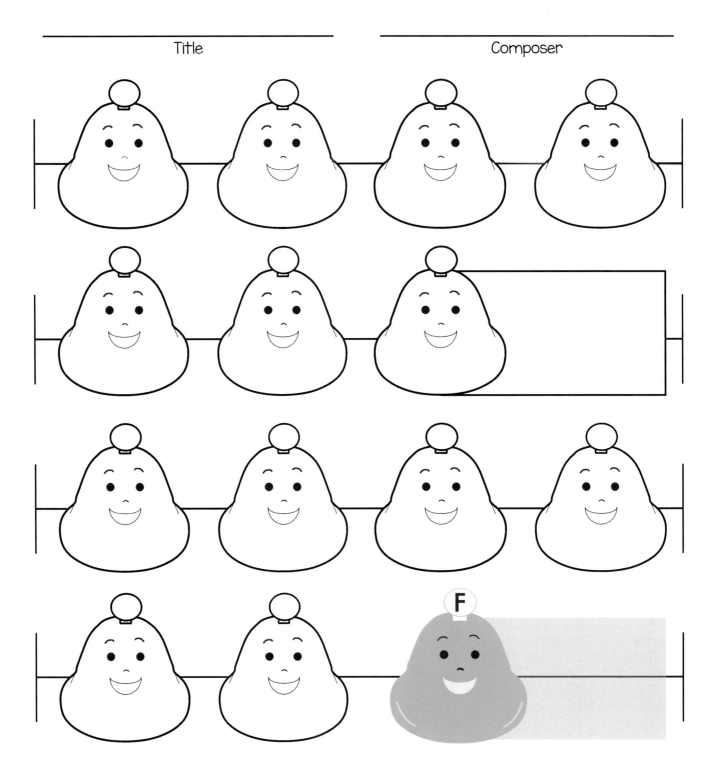

Title   Composer

I-IV Progressions

 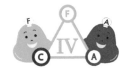

Write 4 short chord patterns using just the I (C chord) and the IV (F chord).
Loop each pattern 4 times and even try singing over your loop! This is how lots of popular music is written.

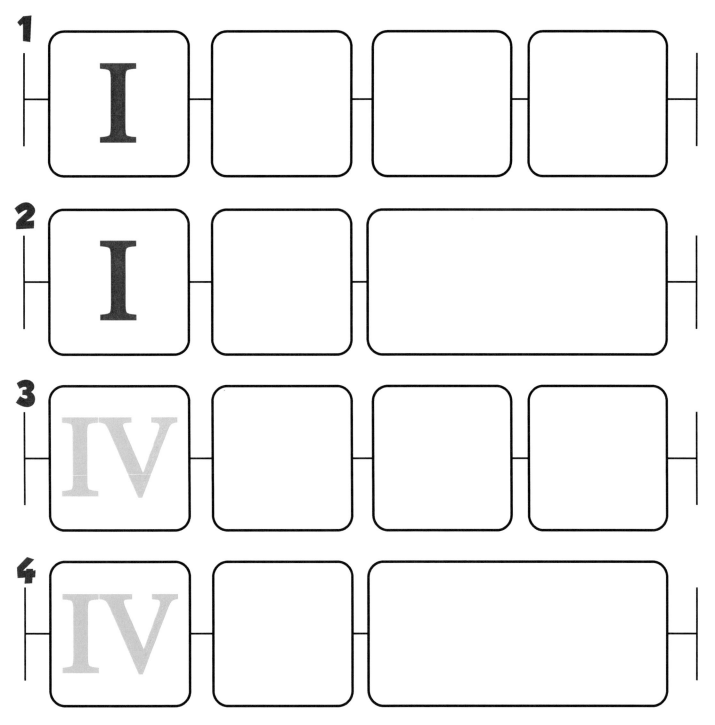

Missing Chord Pieces

Complete each chord triangle by adding the
Roman numeral and note names.

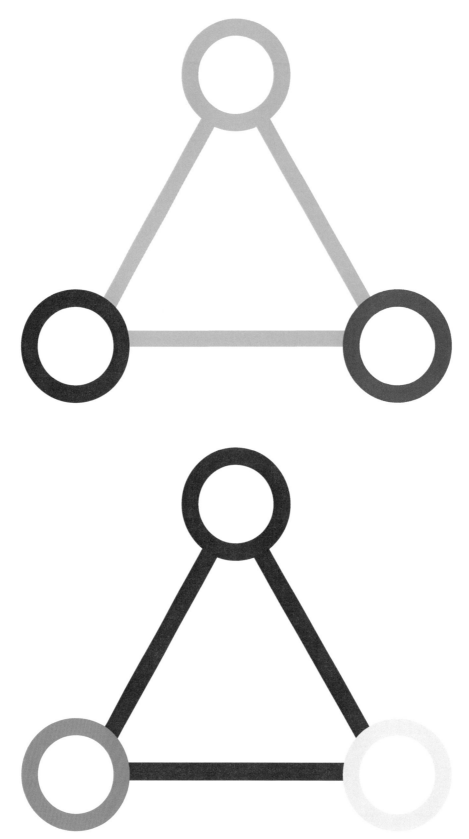

F Cube

Cut along the dotted line. Fold along the inside black lines. Then tape your cube along the edges. Practice vocabulary with your new cube and save it for an activity later this section!

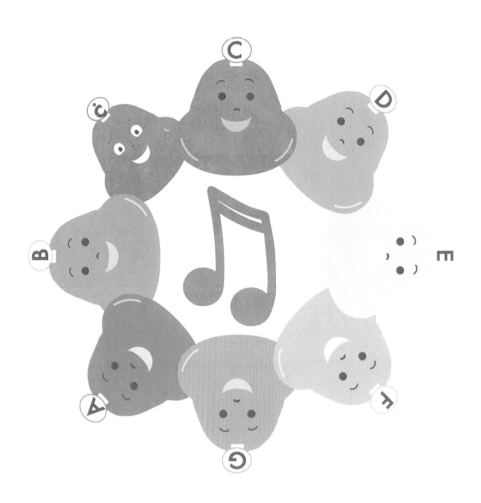

ċ Cube

Cut along the dotted line.
Fold along the inside black
lines. Then tape your cube
along the edges. Practice
vocabulary with your new
cube and save it for
an activity later this section!

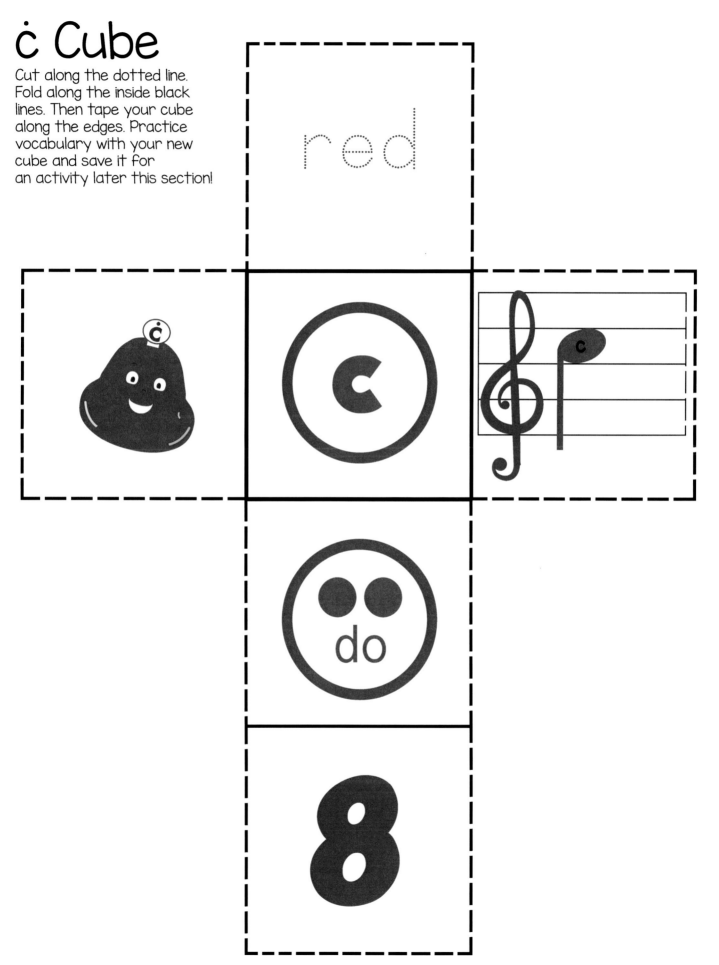

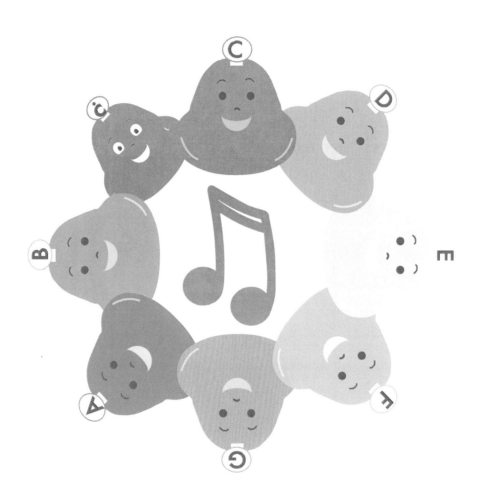

A Cube

Cut along the dotted line. Fold along the inside black lines. Then tape your cube along the edges. Practice vocabulary with your new cube and save it for an activity later this section!

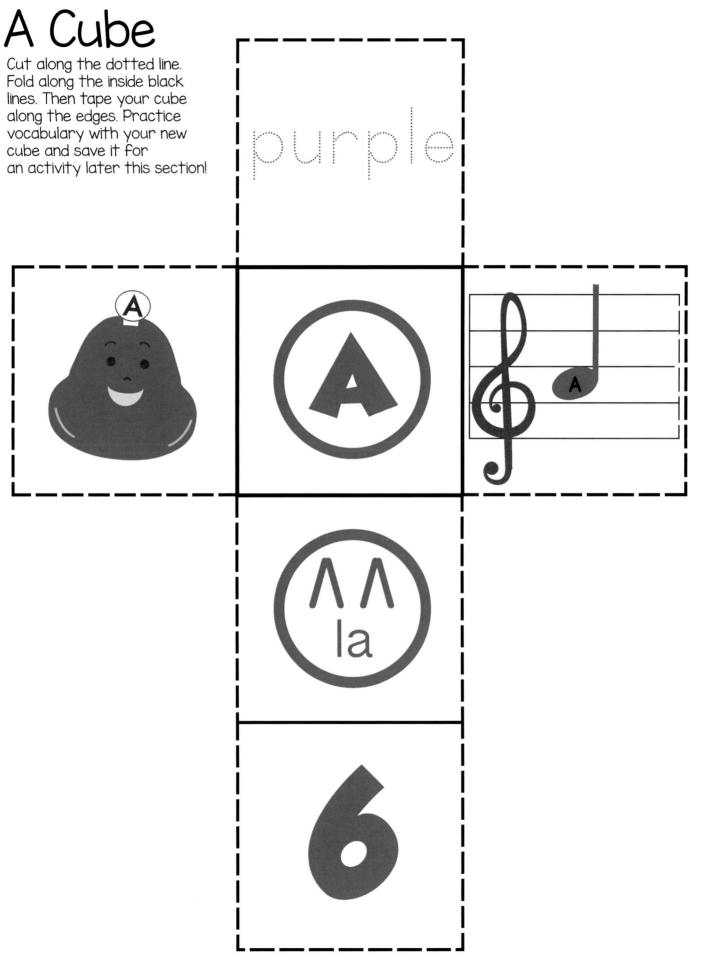

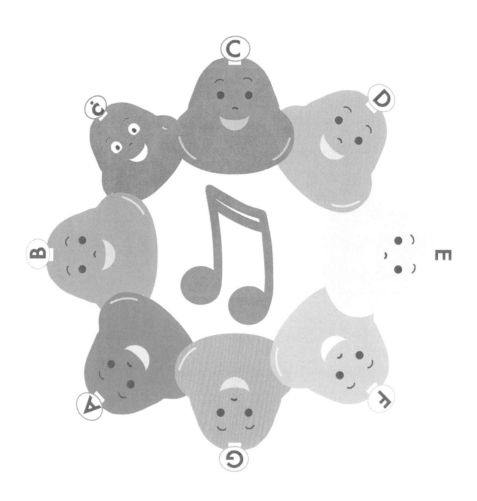

Cube Stacking

With your F, A and c cubes, you can stack them to build different versions of the F chord. Try mixing up the order and which side of the cubes you use!

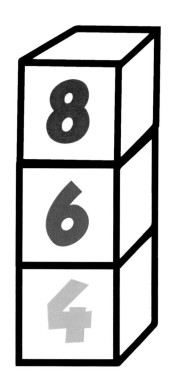

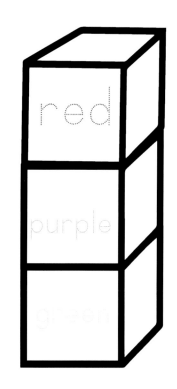

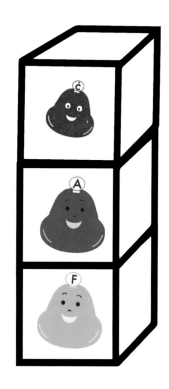

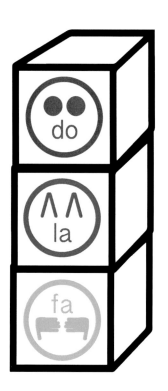

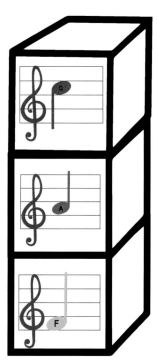

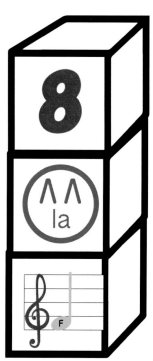

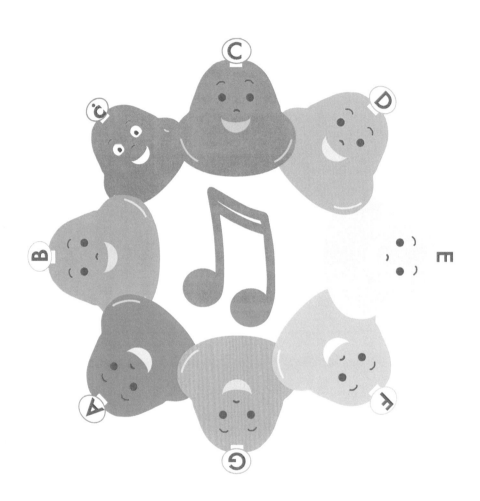

Chapter 7 ♫ Section 2: Sol Ti Re ♫ Lesson Guide

Objective

By the end of this section, students should be able to associate the G major chord with the notes: G, B & D.

Overview

In this section, students learn the G major chord.

Essential Question

How can a student play a G major chord?

Instruction Tips

There is a lot of cutting in this section. You may want to consider asking students or parents to cut out the cubes ahead of time, in order to save time during the lesson.

Materials

- G Bell • B Bell • D Bell
- Teal Crayon • Orange Crayon • Pink Crayon
- Sol Ti Re Video Access
- Workbook pages: 22-35
- Scissors
- Tape

Table of Contents

Sol Ti Re Slide Song Sheets	22
Building the G Chord	25
Write a Song Using the G Chord	26
I-V Progressions	27
G, D & B Cubes	29
Cube Stacking	35

Complementary Activities

Have your students write a song as a class using all of their cubes. Tell them they can add their cubes in any order that they want in order to come up with a collaborative song. At the end, play the song as a class.

Section 7.2 Video Annotations

0:00 Explain to students that this video will use Sol, Ti & Re. They should take out their G, B & D bells.

2:50 Students play two bells at one time instead of just one in order to make a harmony.

3:31 Students play the full G Chord here with all three notes.

4:15 Mr. Rob explains where the G Chord lives and the treble clef.

5:50 Mr. Rob explains the mnemonic device "Every Good Boy Does Fine" for memorizing the notes on the lines of the staff.

Sol Ti Re Slide
Lesson 7.2

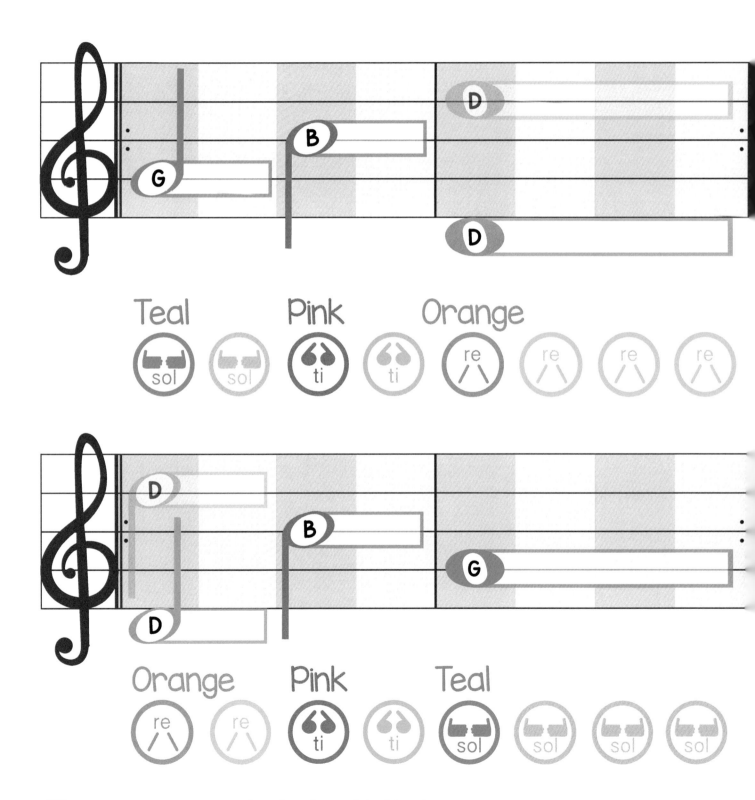

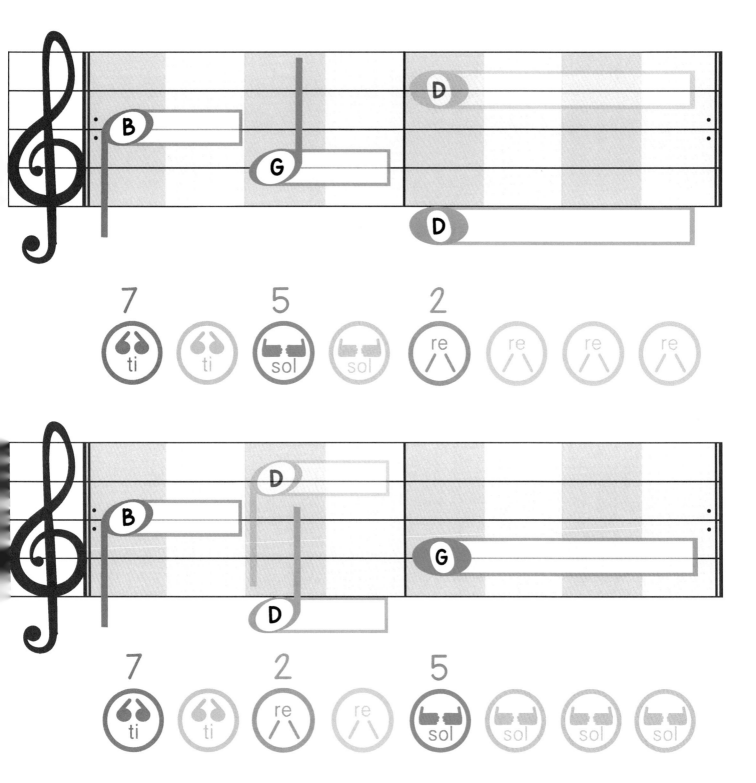

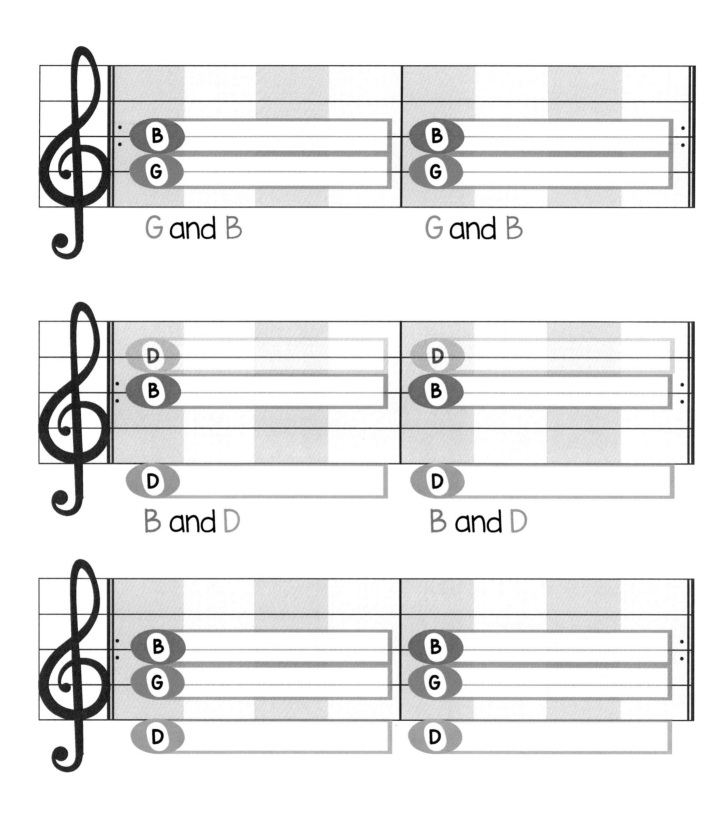

G and B   G and B

B and D   B and D

Building the G Chord

Let's review how we build our G chord.

1. The ROOT NOTE of the G Chord is G. The chord will grow up from there.

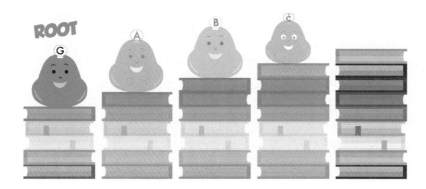

2. From the Root Note, SKIP UP. What note do you land on? This is the next note in your chord. Play these two notes together!

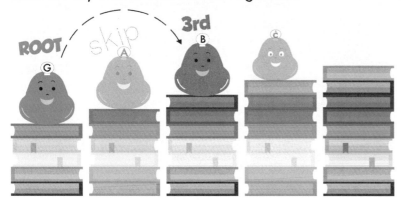

3. Now we need to SKIP UP to find our last note, but what happens when we skip past the note C? Well, because our musical notes repeat in a pattern, we start the pattern over. So the next note after C is D. This is the final note in our chord!

Congratulations!
You built a G Chord.

Write a Song Using

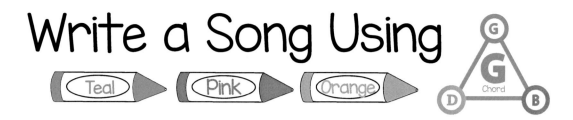

Write a melody using Sol, Ti and Re. Then play it on your instrument.

_____ _____
Title   Composer

I-V Progressions

 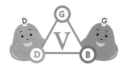

Write 4 short chord patterns using just the I (C chord) and the V (G chord).
Loop each pattern 4 times and even try singing over your loop! This is how
lots of popular music is written.

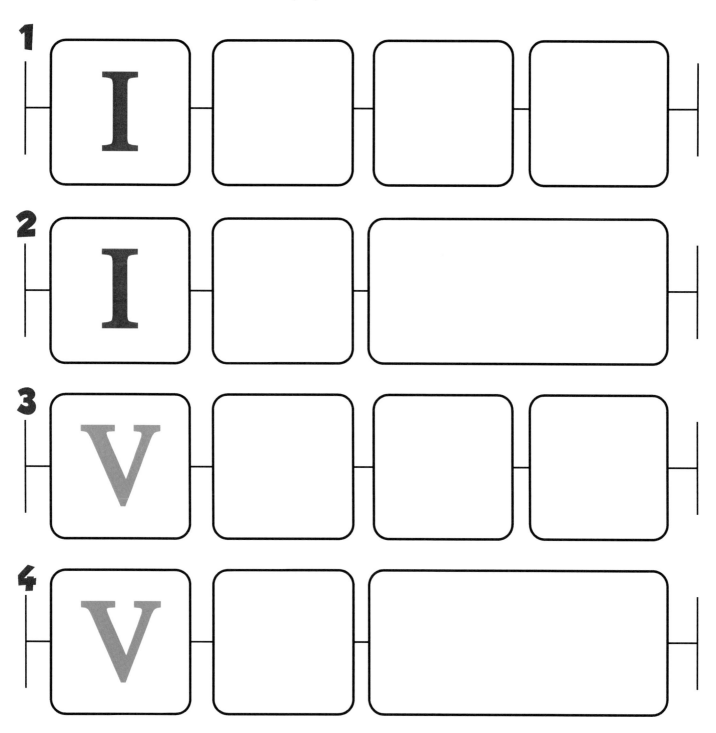

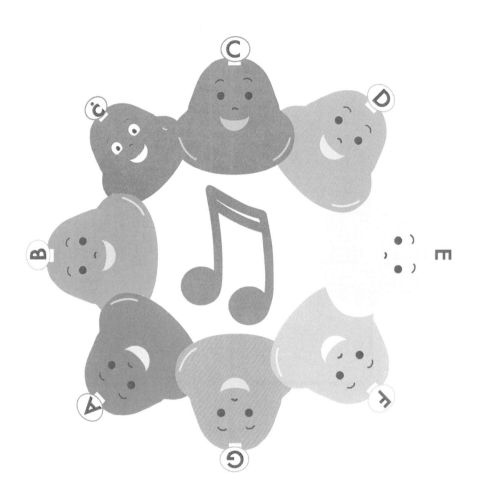

G Cube

Cut along the dotted line. Fold along the inside black lines. Then tape your cube along the edges. Practice vocabulary with your new cube and save it for an activity later this section!

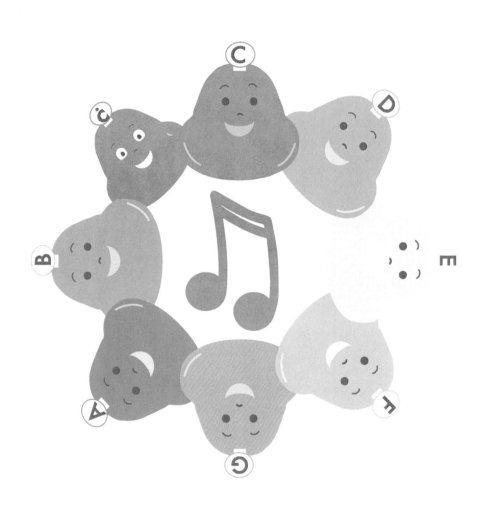

D Cube

Cut along the dotted line. Fold along the inside black lines. Then tape your cube along the edges. Practice vocabulary with your new cube and save it for an activity later this section!

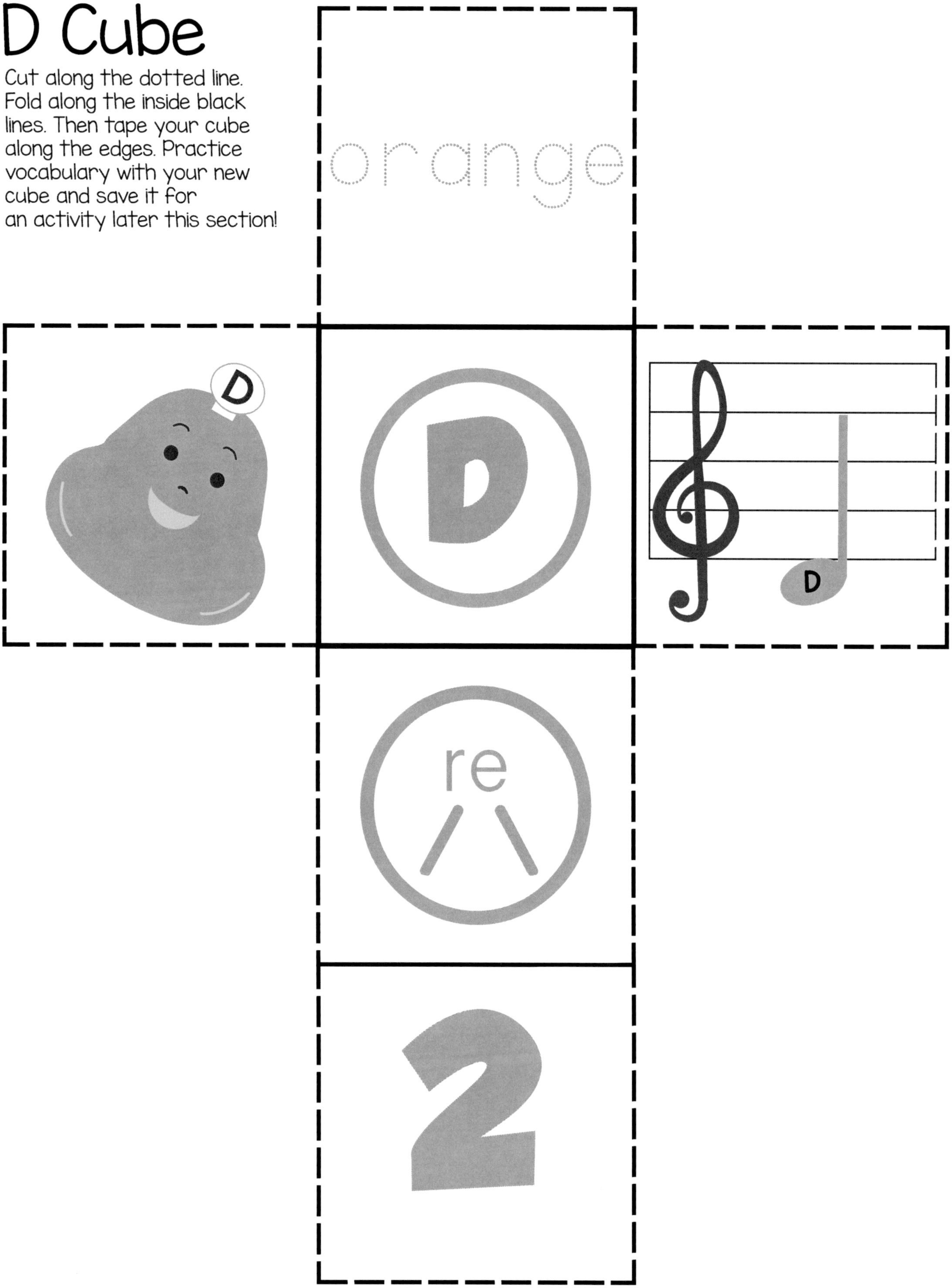

orange

D

re

2

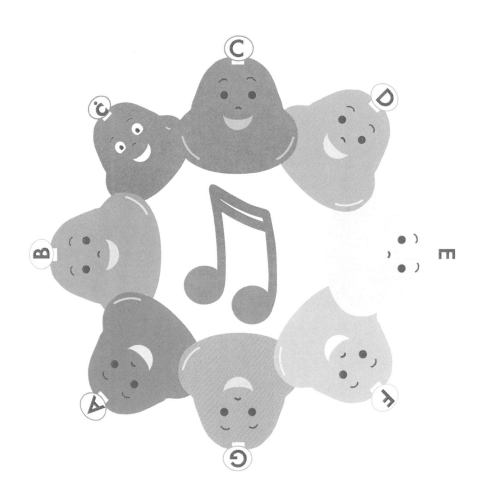

B Cube

Cut along the dotted line. Fold along the inside black lines. Then tape your cube along the edges. Practice vocabulary with your new cube and save it for an activity later this section!

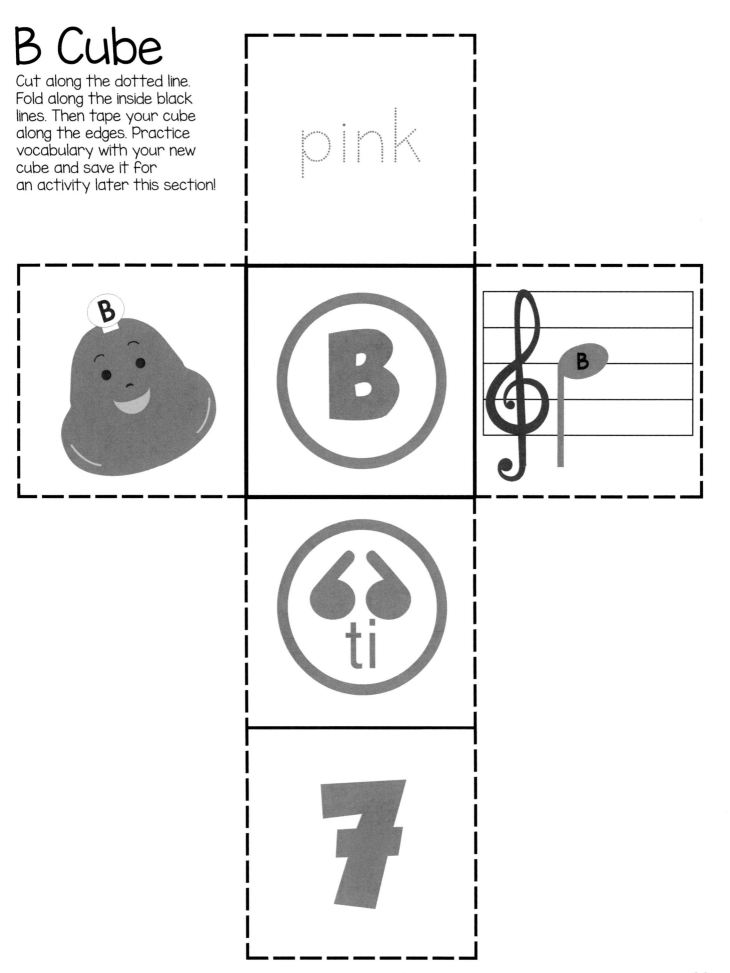

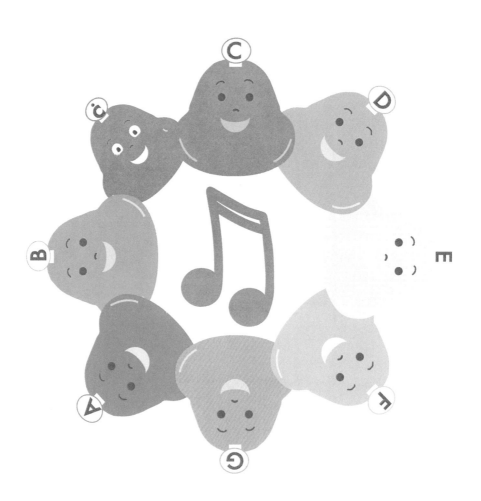

Cube Stacking

Use the cubes you cut out to build chords! You can mix
up the notes however you want, and you will still have the same chord.
Once you've stacked some cubes, try singing and playing your bells in that order.

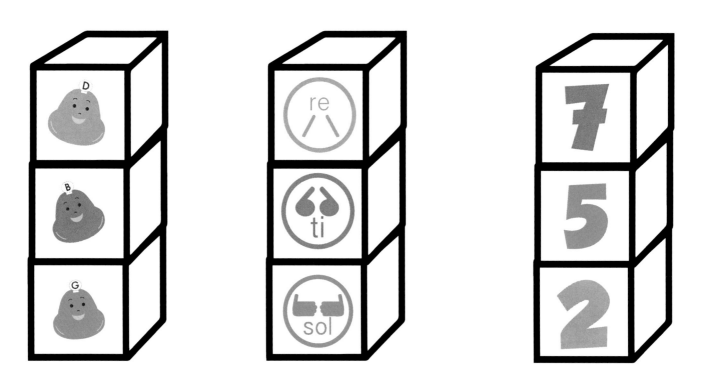

You can stack your cubes to make your own songs. Start on the left and
play the notes going from left to right. Use a steady beat and if you can,
play the stacks at the same time.

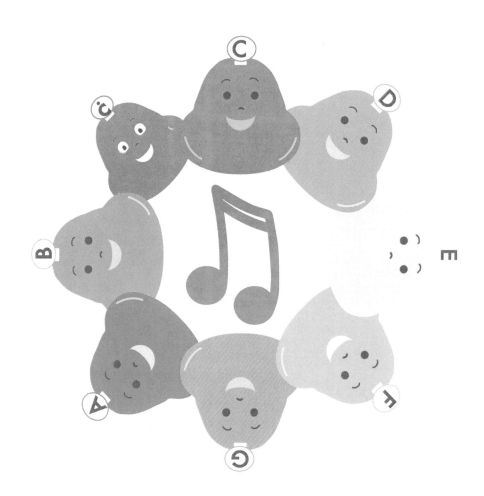

Chapter 7 ♫ Section 3: The Lion Sleeps Tonight ♫ Lesson Guide

Objective

By the end of this section, students should be able to play "The Lion Sleeps Tonight" using chord root notes.

Overview

In this section, students use all three of the chords they know--C, F and G--to play "The Lion Sleeps Tonight".

Essential Question

How can a student use the root notes to play "The Lion Sleeps Tonight"?

Instruction Tips

This song has three different verses, and for younger students, this can be a challenge. Encourage the students to practice singing the songs and trying to read the words, but if they're having trouble, just repeat the first verse.

Materials

- C Bell • F Bell • G Bell
- Red Crayon • Green Crayon
- Teal Crayon
- The Lion Sleeps Tonight Video Access
- Workbook pages: 38-44

Table of Contents

The Lion Sleeps Tonight Song Sheets	38
Chord Building	40
Circle the Root Note	41
Write a Root Note Song	42
Write a Chord Progression	43
Finish the Pattern	44

Complementary Activities

Challenge your learner to play "The Lion Sleeps Tonight" using all three notes of each chord instead of just the root note.

Section 7.3 Video Annotations

0:36 Explain to students that in this video they will play three chords, using three bells in each. Take a minute to review each chord while the chord triangles are on the screen.

0:46 Mr. Rob explains the root note of each chord and that students will only be playing F, G and C.

1:13 Pause here and make sure the students know to play their bell when the animated bell jumps into the water.

2:56 Mr. Rob switches from singing the lyrics to singing the chord names.

3:49 Mr. Rob discusses the pattern of the song--1, 4, 1, 5 and each root note.

The Lion Sleeps Tonight
Lesson 7.3
☆☆☆☆☆

VERSE 1

  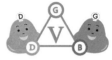

In the jungle, the mighty jungle, the Lion sleeps tonight

 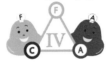 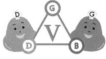

In the jungle, the mighty jungle, the Lion sleeps tonight

CHORUS 1 (SING 2 TIMES)

 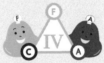

A-weema-weh, a-weema-weh, a-weema-weh, a-weema-weh

A-weema-weh, a-weema-weh, a-weema-weh, a-weema-weh

VERSE 2

 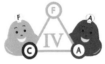 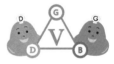

Near the village the peaceful village, the Lion sleeps tonight

 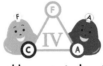 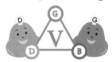

Near the village the quiet village, the Lion sleeps tonight

CHORUS 2 (REPEAT CHORUS 1 TWICE)

Using this chord chart, you can play the whole song all by yourself.

1. First, watch the video until you know the song pretty well. Chord charts are good, but you need to know the song a bit first. You should practice playing, singing, and even reading-along with the video.

2. Then, use just this chart and try playing the song without the video! While playing the 2-note chords, sing the words written underneath. Use the words, or lyrics and your memory of the song to guide you. This is how many musicians learn to read music.

VERSE 3

 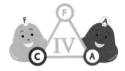  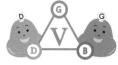

Hush my darling, don't fear my darling, the Lion Sleeps tonight.

 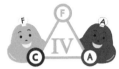  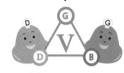

Hush my darling, don't fear my darling, the Lion Sleeps tonight.

CHORUS 3 (SING 2 TIMES)

 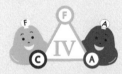

A-weema-weh, a-weema-weh, a-weema-weh, a-weema-weh

 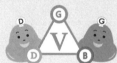

A-weema-weh, a-weema-weh, a-weema-weh, a-weema-weh

ENDING

Chord Building

Can you build the C, F and G chords?
First, draw a skip up from the ROOT note! Circle the bell you land on.
Then, from that note, draw another skip up again and circle the bell you land on.
If you find some bells that repeat in the chord, you can circle those, too.

skip

1. Build the C Chord and circle the bells in the chord.

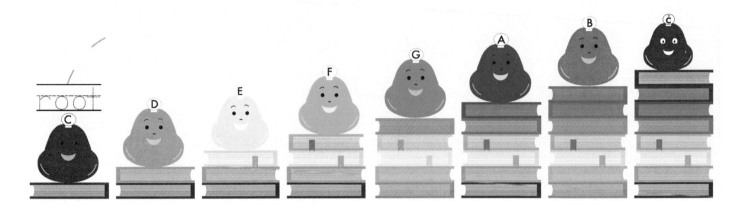

2. Build the F Chord and circle the bells in the chord.

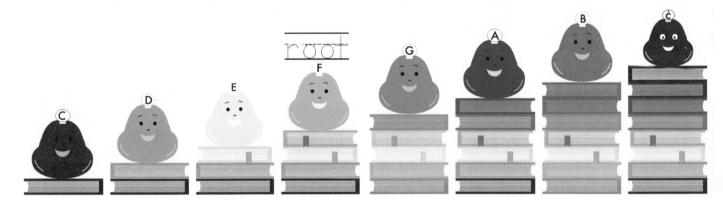

3. Build the G Chord and circle the bells in the chord.

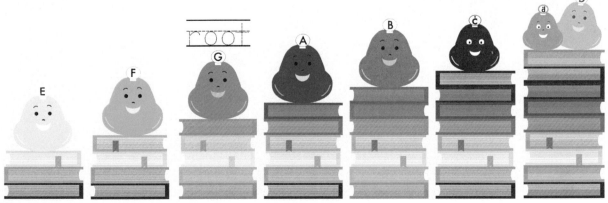

Circle the Root Note

Cirlce the correct root note for each chord number on the line.

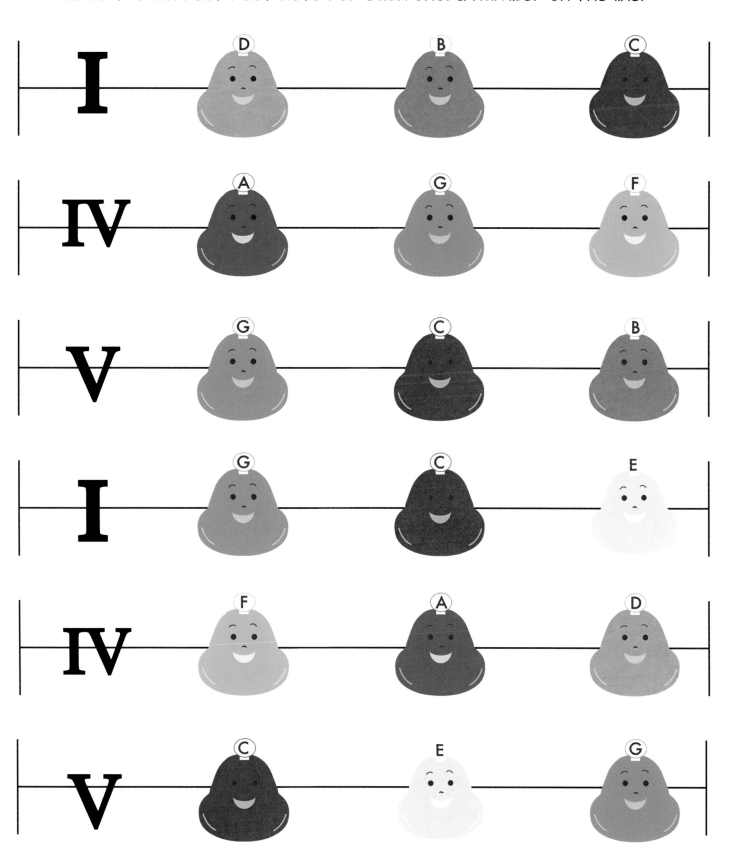

Write a Root Note Song

Title	Composer

Write a Chord Progression

 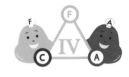 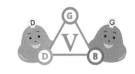

Write one longer progression with I-IV-V. Then play it on your bells!

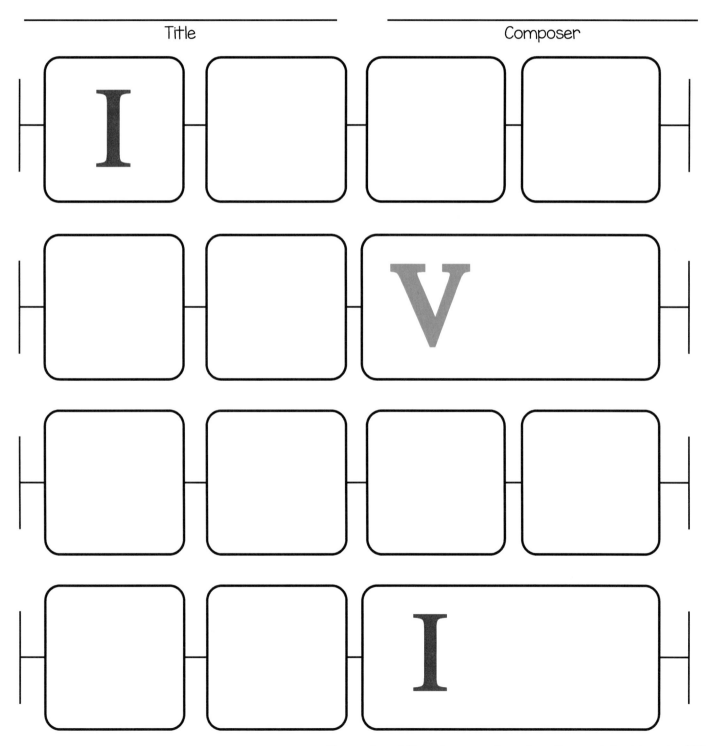

Title

Composer

Finish the Pattern

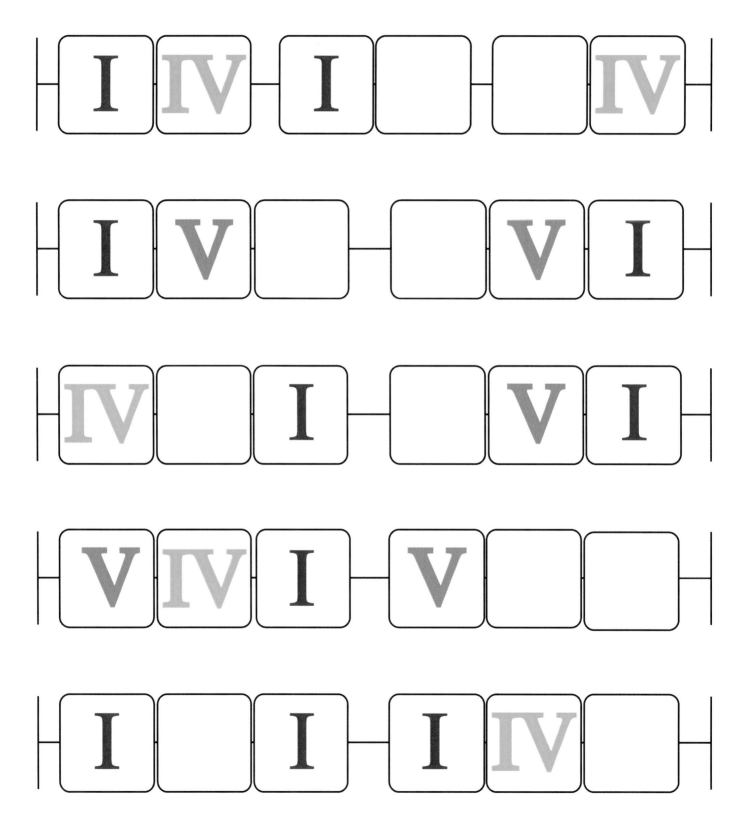

Chapter 7 ♫ Section R: Beet & Avocado ♫ Lesson Guide

Objective

By the end of this section, students will be able to sing "Sweet Beets" using a variety of rhythms.

Overview

In this section, students use a variety of rhythms to play "Sweet Beets".

Essential Question

How can a student use a variety of rhythms to play "Sweet Beets"?

Instruction Tips

Before watching the video, review the names for rhythms you've learned in previous chapters: beet, cherry, avocado, pineapple and shh. In this section, students will review all except for pineapple.

Materials

• Red Crayon
• Beet & Avocado Video Access
• Workbook pages: 46-51

Table of Contents

Beet and Avocado Song Sheets	46
Rhythmic Animals	48
I, IV & V	50
Eighth Note Addition	51

Complementary Activities

Play a call and response pattern using beet, cherry, avocado and shh. Pause the video and allow students to make up their own call & response rhythm sections in Sweet Beets.

Section 7. R Video Annotations

0:00 Explain to students that in this rhythm video, they will sing Sweet Beets using four of the notes they've learned already: Beet, Cherry, Avocado & Shh.

1:35 Mr. Rob reviews the Shh bell or rest.

Beet & Avocado
Lesson 7.R

☆☆☆☆☆

Clap, tap or stomp along while you sing with the sheet music below after
you've watched the Beet & Avocado video in section 7.R.

CHORUS 1

Sweet Beets, we've got some!
If you **want some** Sweet Beets, we've got 'em.
If you want Sweet Beets, we've got some,
If you **want some** Sweet Beets, we've got 'em.

VERSE 1

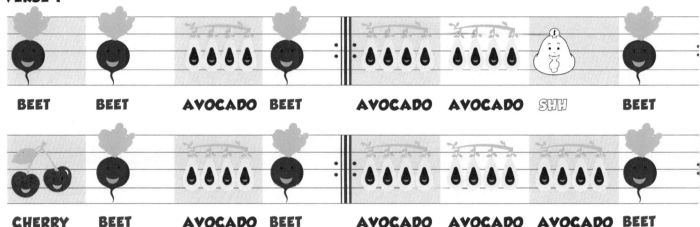

CHORUS 2

Sweet Beets, we've got some!
If you **want some** Sweet Beets, we've got 'em.
If you want Sweet Beets, we've got some,
If you **want some** Sweet Beets, we've got 'em.

VERSE 2

CHORUS 3

Sweet Beets, we've got some!
If you **want some** Sweet Beets, we've got 'em.
If you want Sweet Beets, we've got some,
If you **want some** Sweet Beets, we've got 'em.

VERSE 3

| BEET | BEET | AVOCADO | BEET | CHERRY | CHERRY | AVOCADO | BEET |
| AVOCADO | AVOCADO | SHH | BEET | SHH | AVOCADO | SHH | BEET |

CHORUS 4

Sweet Beets, we've got some!
If you **want some** Sweet Beets, we've got 'em.
If you want Sweet Beets, we've got some,
If you **want some** Sweet Beets, we've got 'em.

CHORUS 5

Sweet Beets, we've got some!
If you **want some** Sweet Beets, we've got 'em.
If you want Sweet Beets, we've got some,
If you **want some** Sweet Beets, we've got 'em.

Rhythmic Animals
Below are some of the rhythmic animals we saw in earlier chapters!
Try reading the names of the animals as you tap the rhythm of the names on your legs.
Use a slow metronome (60 bpm) to keep time. Repeat each line 4 times before moving onto the next line or use call and response to work through them together.

Challenge: If you have a favorite song about animals, sing the chorus of that song in between the different lines of the animal rhythms.

I, IV & V

Let's count treble clefs!

If the number of clefs is the same as the Roman numeral above it, circle them.
If the number of clefs does NOT match, draw an X through them.

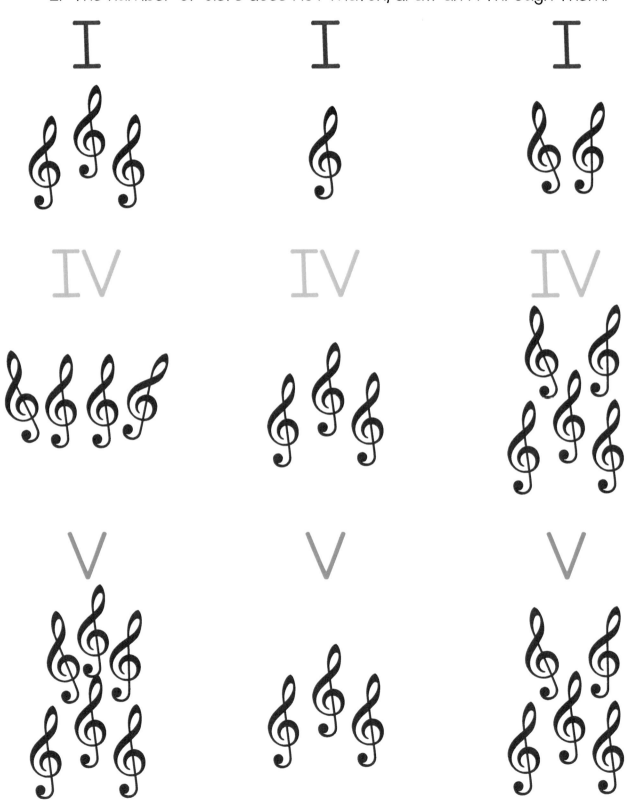

Eighth Note Addition

When we have two eighth notes together, we normally write them like this:

If you want split up the eighth notes, then they look like this:

Don't forget that it takes 2 eighth notes to fill up one beat. = = 1 Beat

On this page, circle all the pairs of eighth notes. Then write a 1 underneath them.

Then, add up the 1s in each line to figure out the total number of beats in the measure.

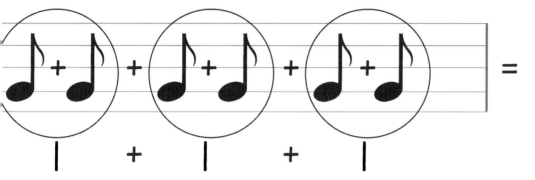

1   +   1   +   1

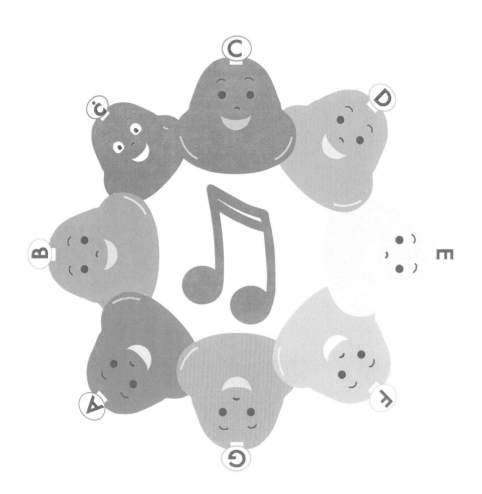

Chapter 7 ♫ Section 4: Blues in C Major ♫ Lesson Guide

Objective

By the end of this section, students should be able to play a blues song using the I, IV and V chord.

Overview

In this section, students use the I, IV and V chord to play a classic blues song.

Essential Question

How can a student use the I, IV and V chord to play the blues?

Instruction Tips

As you complete the activities, play the bells, or encourage your student to play the bells. Each time they use a teal crayon, encourage them to tap the G bell as well.

Materials

- Full Set of C Major Deskbells
- Full Set of Crayons
- Blues in C Major Video Access
- Workbook pages: 54-65
- Scissors

Table of Contents

Blues in C Major Song Sheets   54

16 Bar Blues Chord Pattern   58

Chord Building   59

Hand-Sign Blues   61

Hand-Sign Paths   65

Complementary Activities

Ask students to share their original songs with the class. The class could play along in a call and response way with the student-composer leading or help each other write lyrics for one anothers' songs.

Section 7.4 Video Annotations

0:00 Explain to students that in this video they will play a song using all 8 of their bells, but that they will start with just the hand-signs.

1:36 Students begin hand-signing following along with Mr. Rob.

3:06 Mr. Rob switches from singing Solfège hand-signs to singing note names and playing the bells.

2:35 Students play and sing along with Mr. Rob instead of using the call and response format.

5:12 Mr. Rob reviews the chords played in this video.

Blues in C Major
Lesson 7.4

☆☆☆☆☆

The Blues is a VERY popular chord progression. Try playing it 4 times. Start by singing about the colors, then try again with the letters, then the numbers and finally with the Solfège hand-signs!

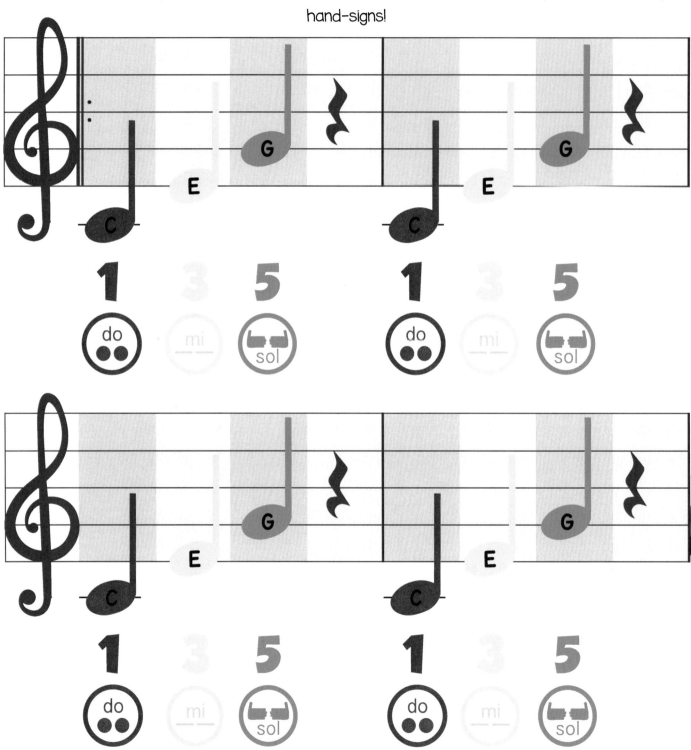

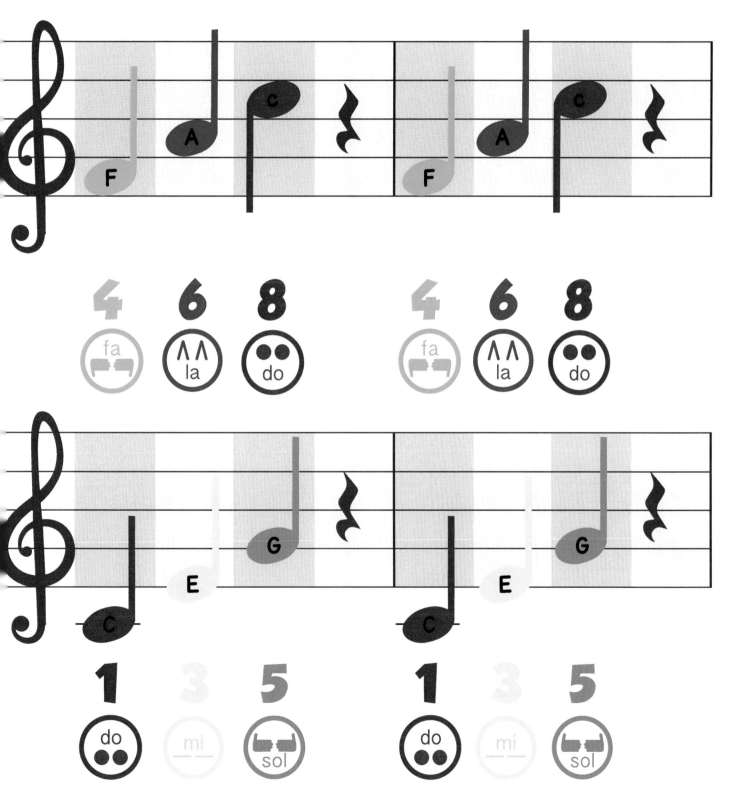

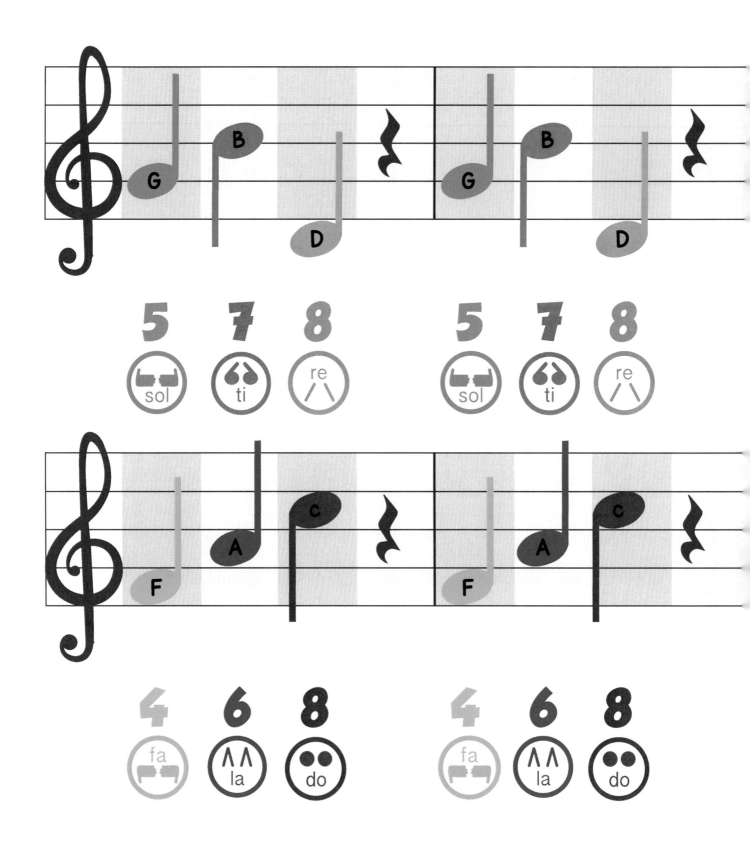

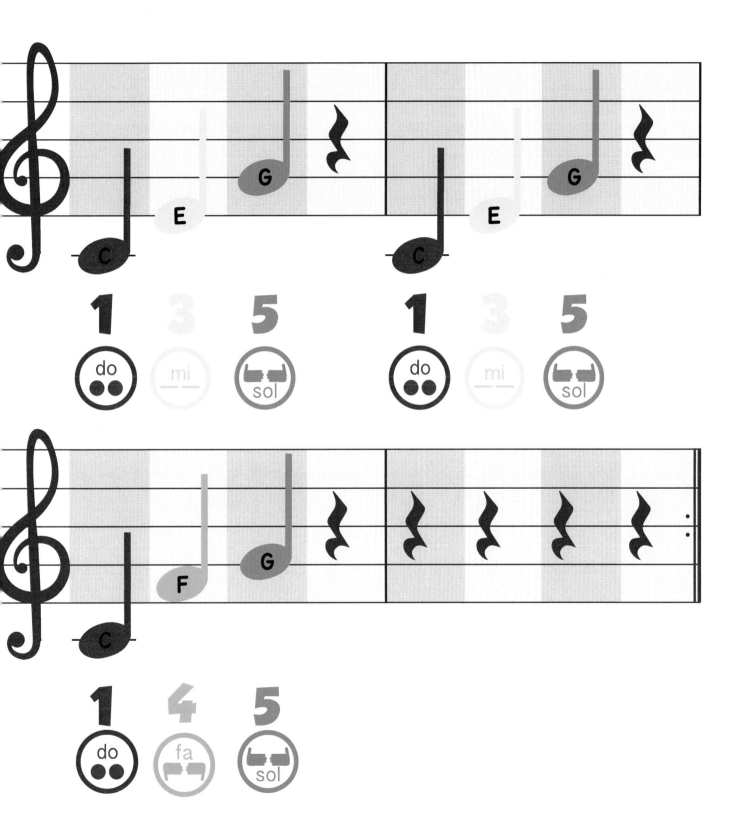

16 Bar Blues Chord Pattern

The chord chart below is a simple way to read the blues.
Try playing the chords and singing your own song on top of the chords.
Each box is one measure long. You can play steady quarter notes or have some extra
fun by changing up your rhythms a bit.

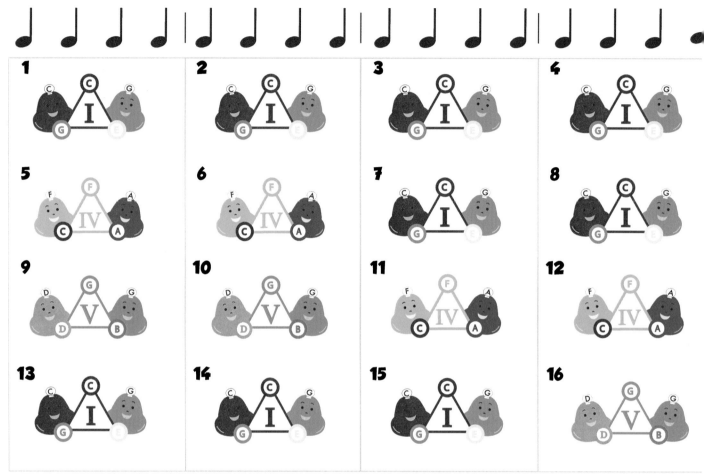

Ready to sing the Blues? Write your own lyrics on the lines below and sing them while you
play the chords above.

_____

_____

_____

Chord Building

Can you build the C, F and G chords?
First, draw a skip up from the ROOT note! Circle the bell you land on.
Then, from that note, draw another skip up again and circle the bell you land on.
If you find some bells that repeat in the chord, you can circle those, too.

1. Build the C Chord and circle the bells in the chord.

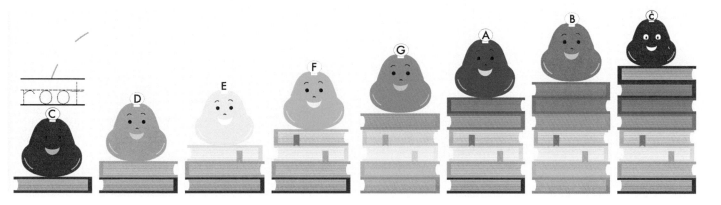

2. Build the F Chord and circle the bells in the chord.

3. Build the G Chord and circle the bells in the chord.

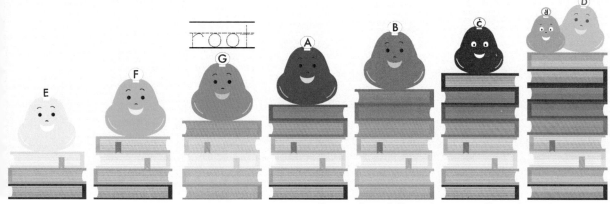

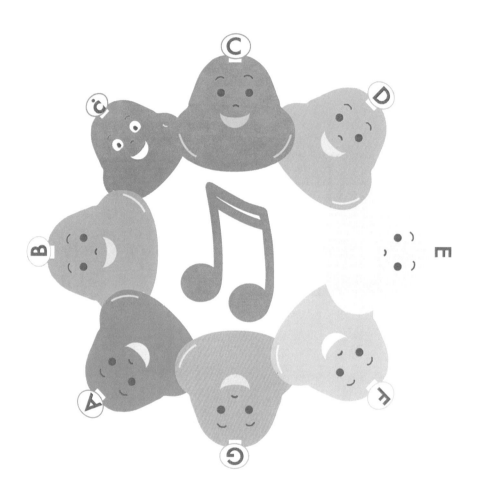

Hand-Sign Blues

Without the help of your bells, see if you can sing and hand-sign the blues!

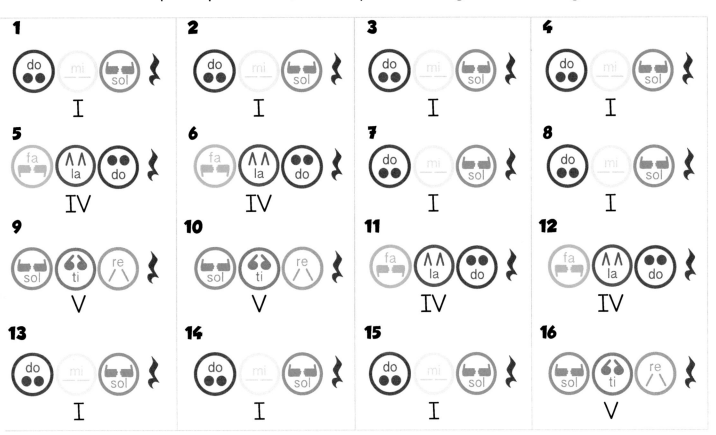

You can cut out these bigger cards below and use them to make your own hand-sign patterns!

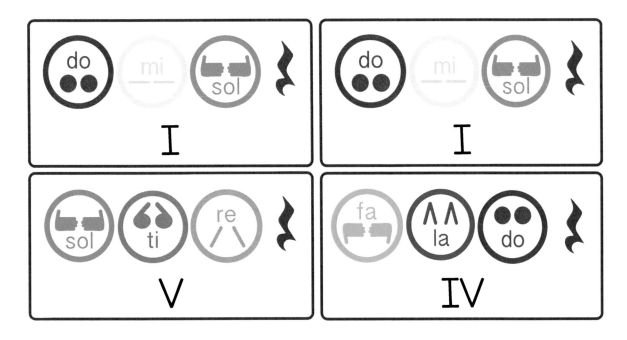

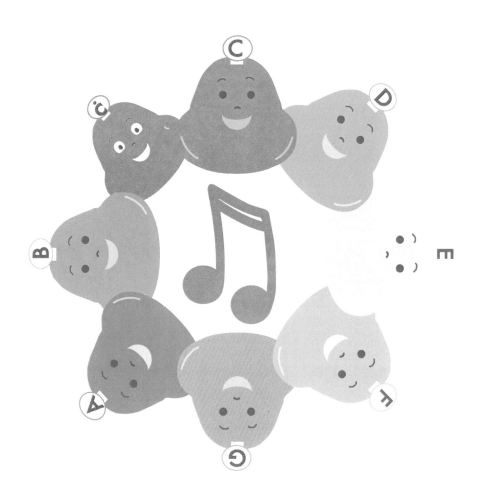

Cut out these hand-sign cards and make your own Hand-Sign Blues!

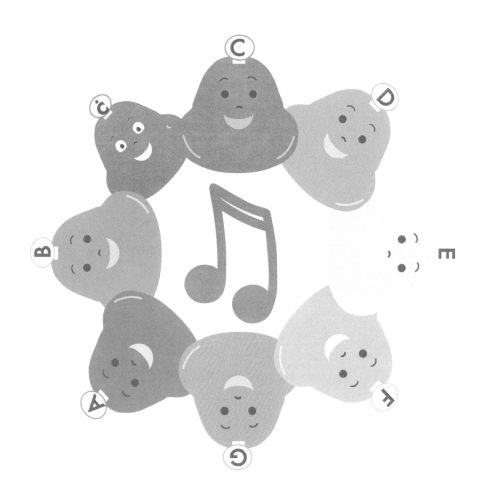

Hand-Sign Paths

Trace the correct path of the Solfège hand signs.

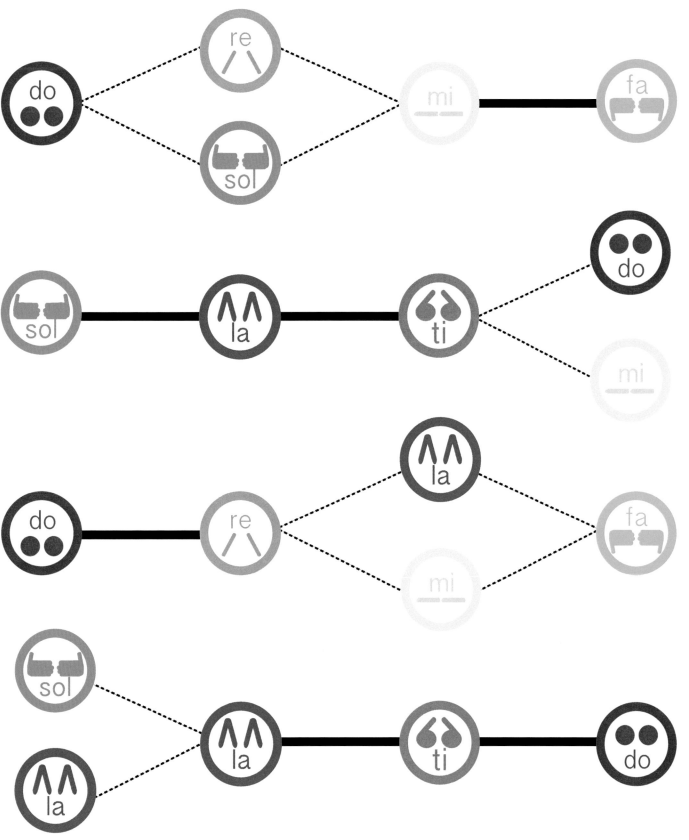

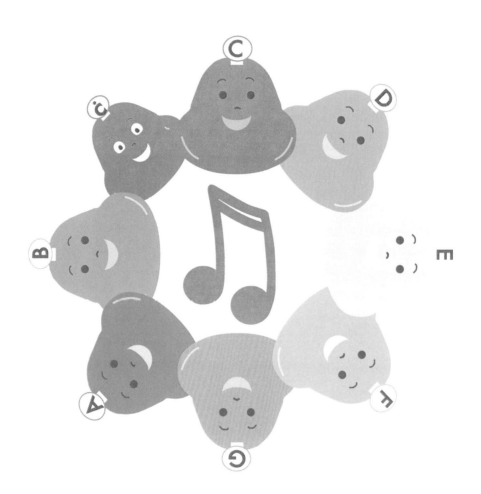

Objective

By the end of this section, students should be able to differentiate between the C chord and the F chord.

Overview

In this section, students practice differentiating between the C chord and the F chord.

Essential Question

How can a student distinguish between the I chord and the IV chord?

Instruction Tips

Hang the chord flash cards from previous sections up in your music practice space. These graphics are a great resource for your learner as they learn to differentiate chords.

Materials

- C Bell • E Bell • G Bell • F Bell • A Bell • c Bell
- Red Crayon • Yellow Crayon • Teal Crayon
- Green Crayon • Purple Crayon
- Chord Watching III Video Access
- Workbook pages: 68-76
- Scissors
- Tape or Glue
- Popsicle Sticks

Table of Contents

Chord Watching III Song Sheets	68
Chord Cards	71
Record the Chord	75
Complete the Chord Triangles	76

Complementary Activities

Put your learners in pairs to play a listening game together. One learner uses his or her chord flash cards, and the other sits with the bells hidden and plays the C, F and G chords.

Section 7.5 Video Annotations

0:00 Explain to students that in this video they will be listening for the C Major Chord and the F Major Chord. Instead of playing the bells, they will try to distinguish between these two chords.

2: 09 Pause here to review the nad placement to indicate a C Major Chord (heart) and an F Major Chord (shoulders).

4:55 Mr. Rob reviews why these chord listening exercises are important and the chords we learned so far: C Major, F Major and G Major.

Chord Watching III
Lesson 7.5
☆☆☆☆☆

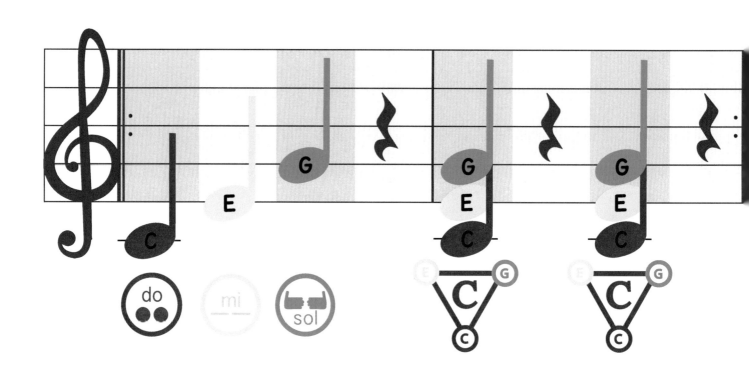

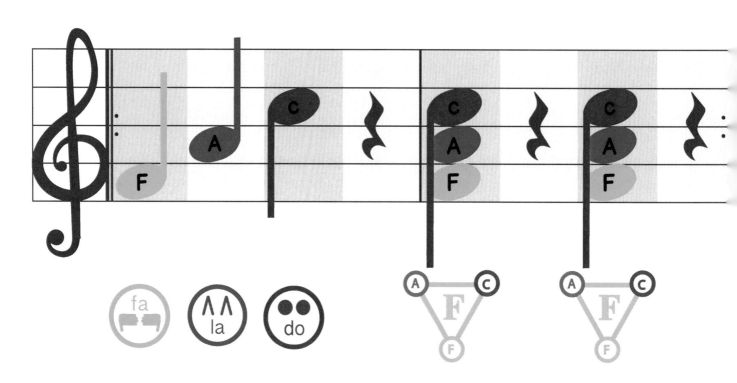

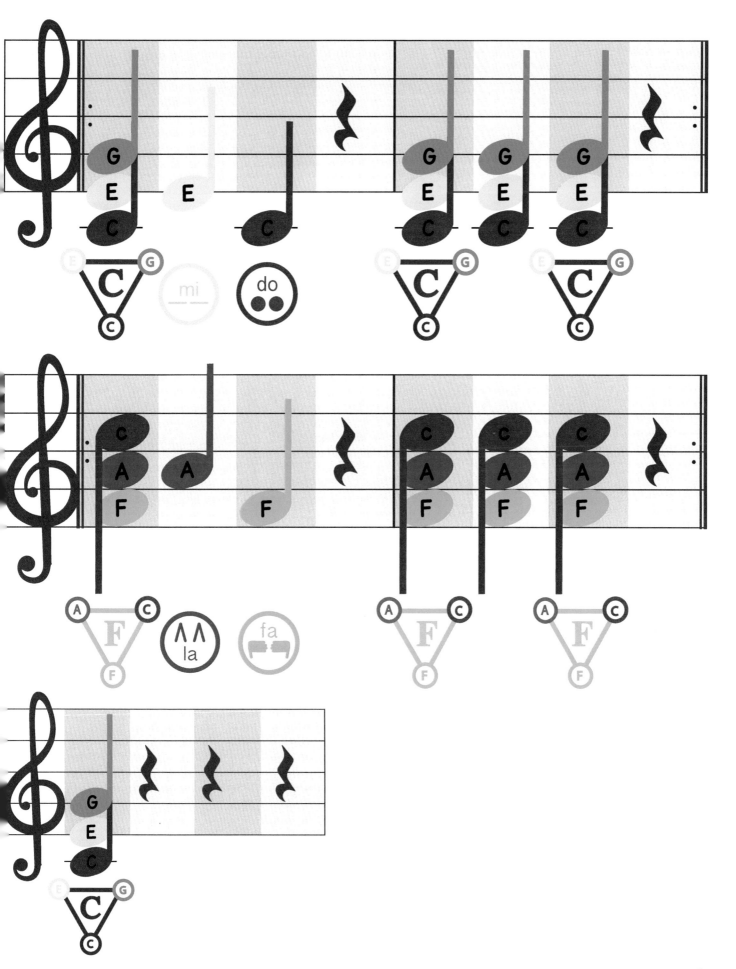

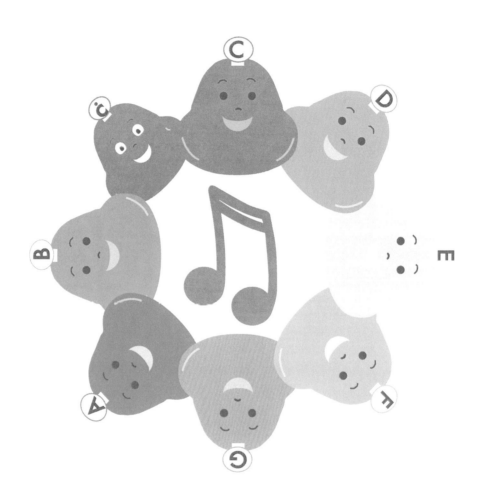

Chord Cards

Cut out the rectangles below. Then fold along the middle line and tape/glue a popsicle stick on the inside.

Now you can continue to play listening games like "Chord Listening" and "What Chord Is It?" with these cards.

Have one player play chords on the bells, while the other players try to guess the chords. Raise up your chord cards to show your answer!

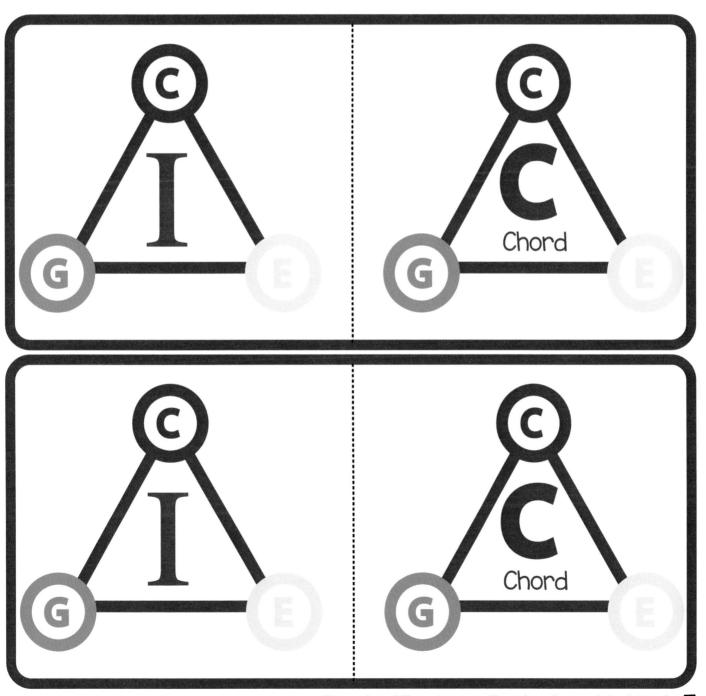

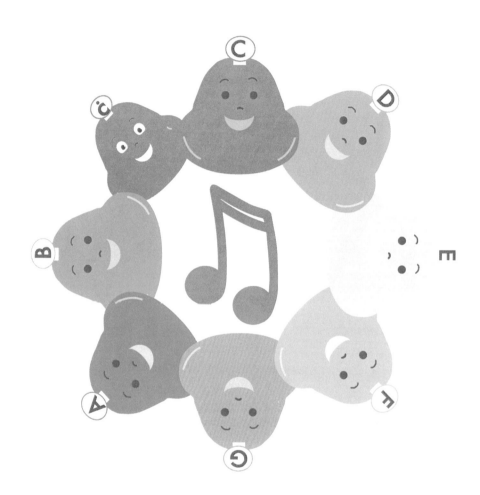

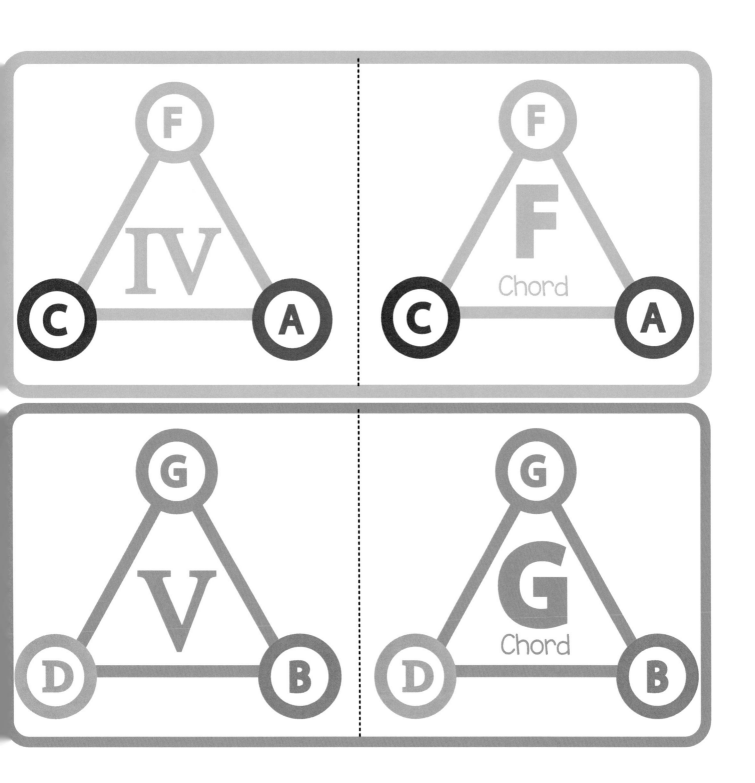

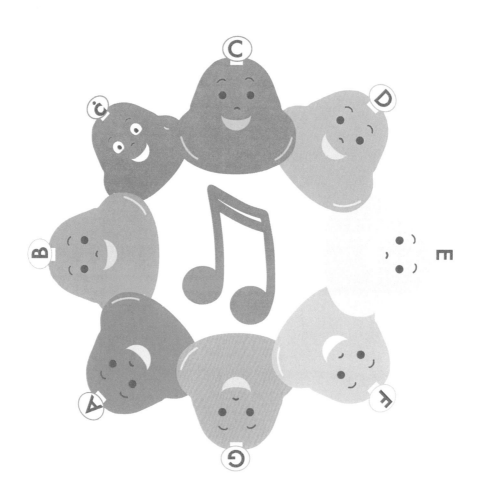

Record the Chord!

In this activity, Player 1 plays the bells while Player 2 listens. Then Player 1 plays either a C or F chord. Player 2 records what they hear.

Use the Roman numerals I and IV to record your answer. If Player 2 is having an easy time identifying the chords, Player 1 can try some individual bells.

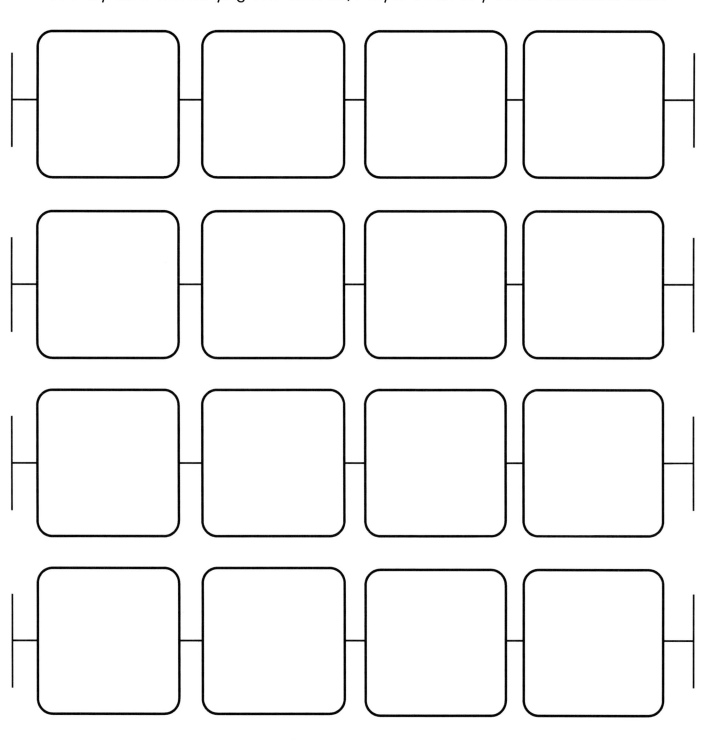

Complete the Chord Triangles

Oh no! The C, F & G chord triangles have lost their parts! Can you help each triangle become complete by tracing a line to each missing piece?

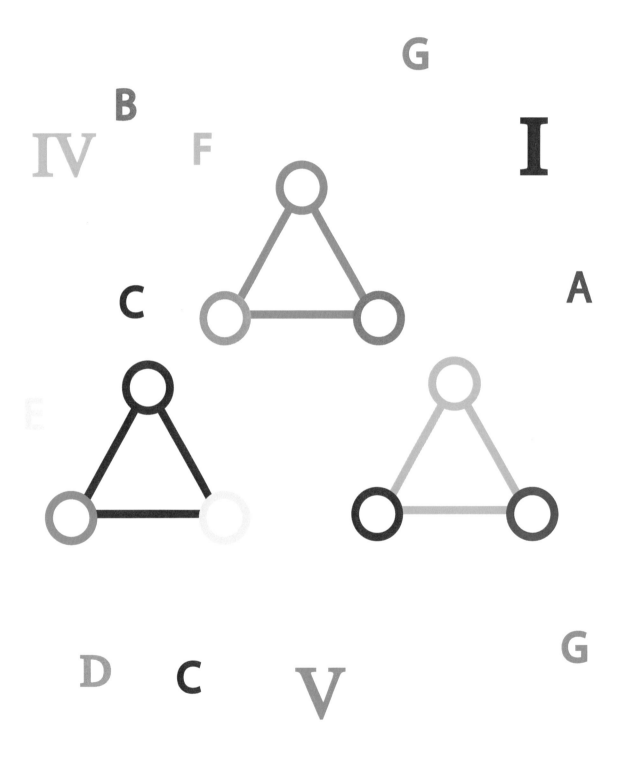

Chapter 7 ❀ Section 6: Chord Watching IV ❀ Lesson Guide

Objective

By the end of this section, students should be able to differentiate between the C Chord, F Chord & G Chord.

Overview

In this section, students practice differentiating between the C chord, F Chord and G Chord.

Essential Question

How can a student distinguish between the I Chord, IV Chord and V Chord?

Instruction Tips

Some students may have trouble playing three notes at the same time. Give them a few chances to experiment with different hand positions or bell arrangments, to find what is most comfortable.

Materials

- Full Set of C Major Deskbells
- Full Set of Crayons
- Chord Watching IV Video Access
- Workbook pages: 78-83

Table of Contents

Chord Watching IV Song Sheets	78
Label the Notes	80
Record the Chord	81
Circle Each Chord	82
Numbers, Bells & Signs	83

Complementary Activities

Put your learners in pairs to play a listening game together. One learner uses his or her chord flash cards, and the other sits with the bells hidden and plays the C, F and G chords.

Section 7. 6 Video Annotations

0:00 Explain to students that in this video they will be listening for the C Major Chord, the F Major Chord and the G Major chord. Instead of playing the bells, they will try to distinguish between these three chords.

0:54 Pause here and give students the chance to guess the chord before Mr. Rob reveals it.

1:14 Pause here and give students the chance to guess the chord before Mr. Rob reveals it.

4:28 Mr. Rob reviews all three chords and the videos that contain those chords for additional practice.

Chord Watching IV
Lesson 7.6

☆☆☆☆☆

Practice this I – IV – V – IV progression to become familiar with the sounds of the chords.

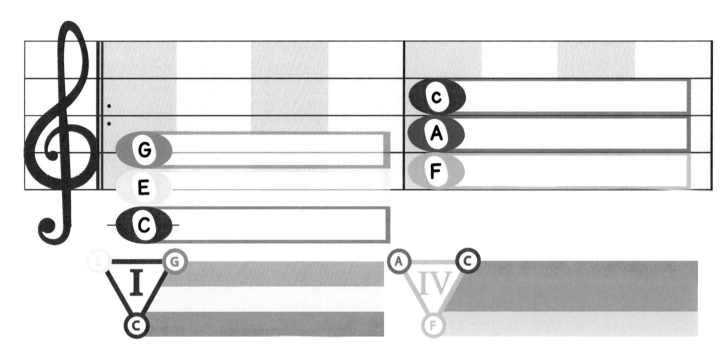

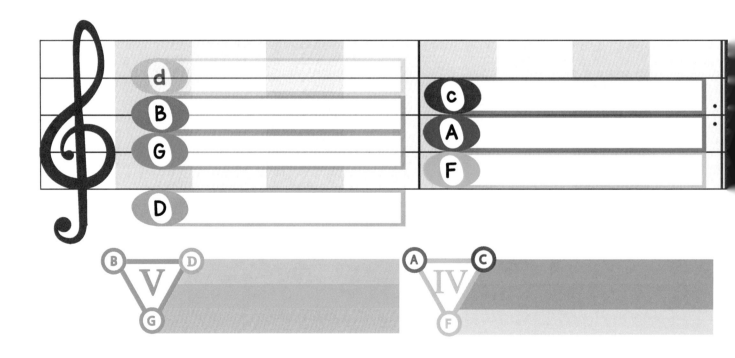

Note: the music below shows the note D two times! The D on the top helps us see the whole chord in a nice stack. The D at the bottom is a lower D, which is bell #2 if you have the C Major Deskbells. The musical notes repeat in a pattern from A-G, and you should experiment with playing higher or lower versions of the notes in your chords!

This progression is a little different. It's a V – IV – I. Try looping this page and singing your own song on top of the chords!

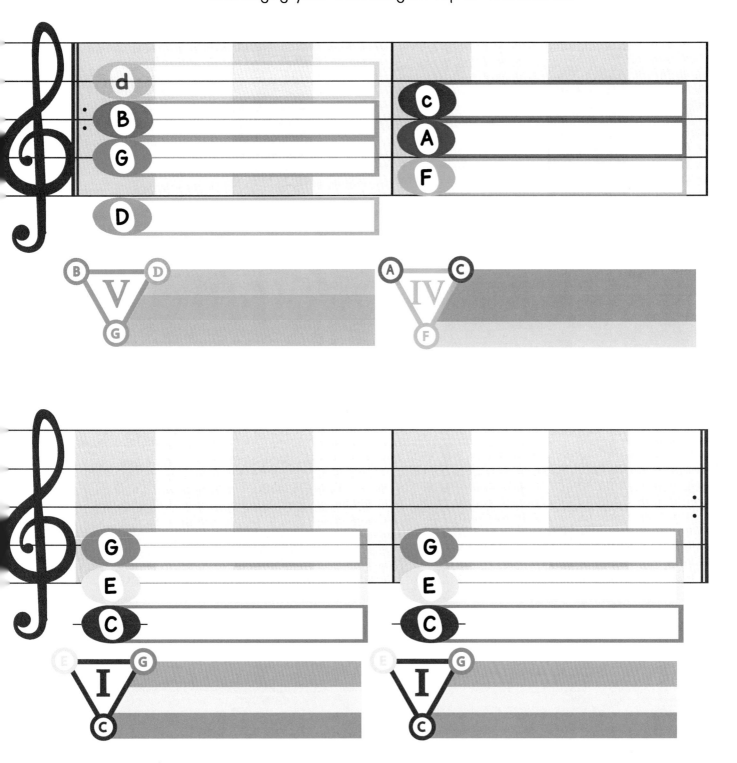

Label the Notes

All of the notes have lost their names!
Can you write the correct name on each note?

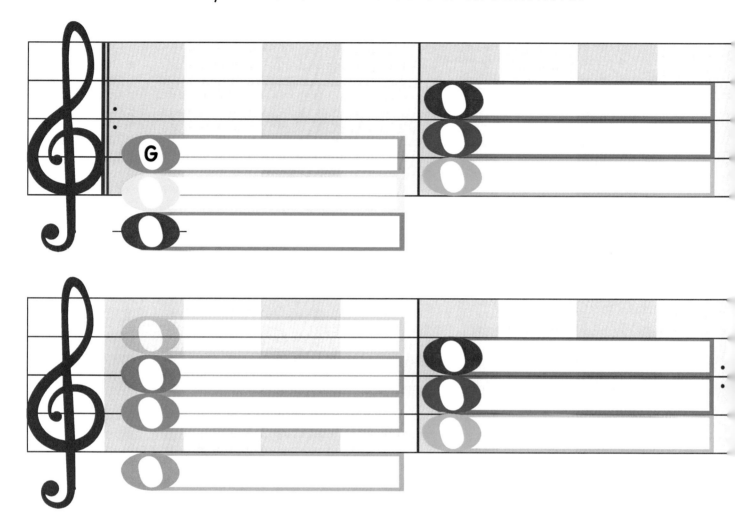

Challenge: These notes have even lost their color! Can you figure out which notes they are? Write the letter names in the note head!

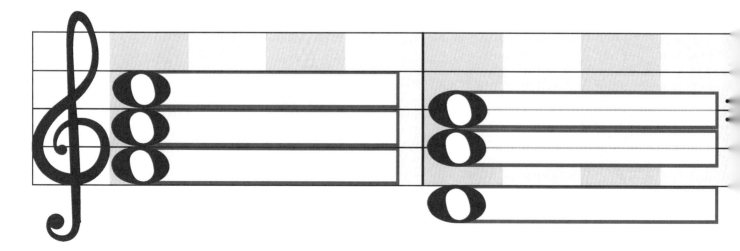

Record the Chord!

In this activity, Player 1 plays the bells while Player 2 listens. Then Player 1 plays either a I (C), IV (F) or V (G) chord. Player 2 records what they hear.

Use the Roman numerals I, IV and V to record your answer. If Player 2 is having an easy time identifying the chords, Player 1 can try some individual bells.

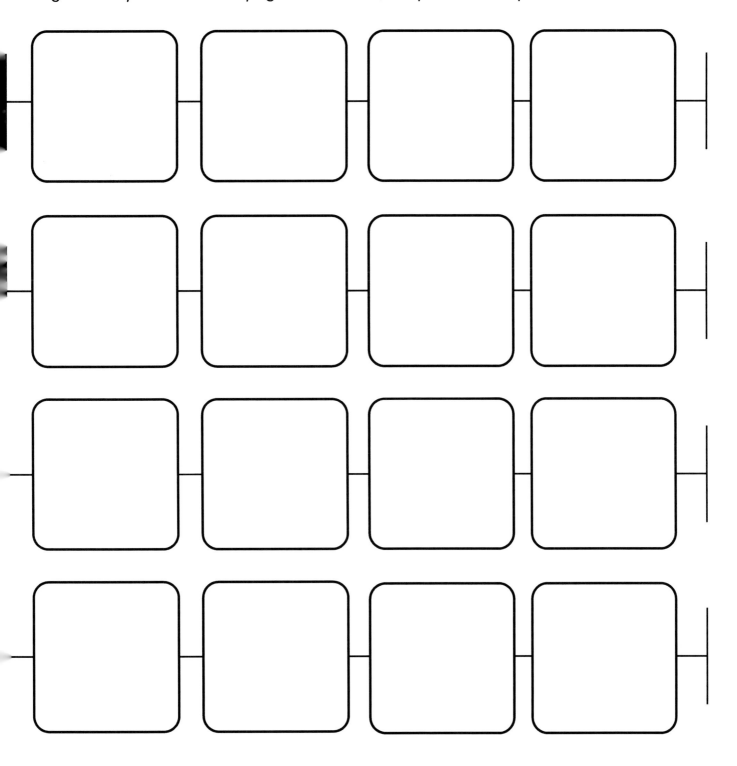

Circle Each Chord
Circle the bells that make up the chord printed on each line.

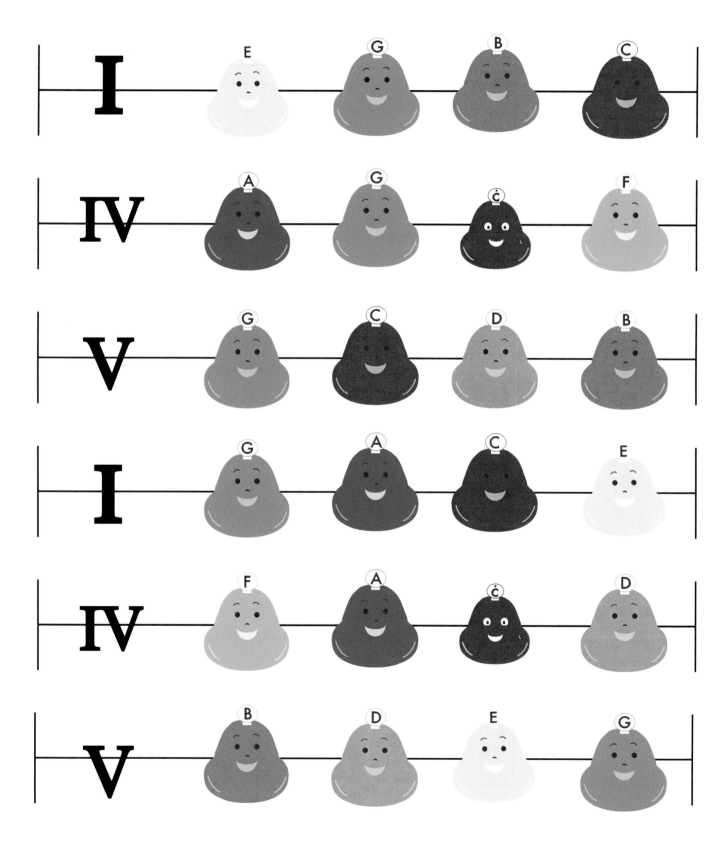

Numbers, Bells & Signs

Connect each number to its bell, then each bell to its hand-sign.

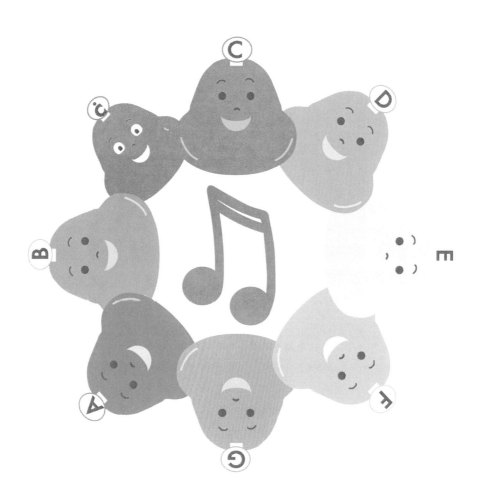

Chapter 7 ♫ Section L: What Chord Is It? ♫ Lesson Guide

Objective

By the end of this section, students should be able to differentiate betewen the I Chord, the IV Chord and the V Chord.

Overview

This section is a listening game. Students will guess between the I Chord, the IV Chord and the V Chord.

Essential Question

How can a student differentiate between the C chord, the F Chord and the G Chord?

Instruction Tips

If your students want to play this listening game several times, instead of having them fill out the worksheet, tell them to hold up their C Chord, G Chord and F Chord cards from earlier in the chapter.

Materials

- Red Crayon • Green Crayon • Teal Crayon
- What Chord Is It? Video Access
- Workbook pages: 86

Table of Contents

What Chord Is It?   86

Complementary Activities

Make up your own listening game with the C Chord, the G Chord and the F Chord.. You could even add in a call and response element by adding patterns.

Section 7L Video Annotations

1:05 Pause and let your learner guess the first chord name before Mr. Rob reveals it!

1:25 Pause and let your learner guess the second chord name before Mr. Rob reveals it!

1:48 Pause and let your learner guess the third note name before Mr. Rob reveals it! Explain to students that this will be the last time you pause before moving on. Be sure that your learner is circling his or her guesses on the What Note Is It workbook page.

Chord Watching IV

As you watch Chapter 7's "What Chord Is It?" use the page below to circle your answers!

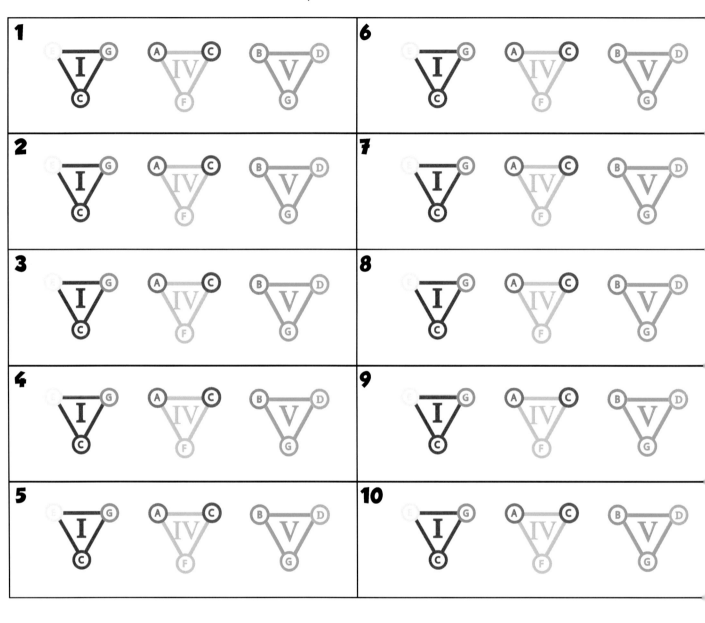

Prodigies Playground

CONGRATULATIONS

You've Completed

Preschool Prodigies

CHAPTER 7

Nice work!

Date

Teacher Signature

49527315R00051

Made in the USA
Columbia, SC
23 January 2019